MW00633957

ANTON OTTO FISCHER

THE SATURDAY EVENING POST

# Book of the Sea and Ships

*The Curtis Publishing Company*
*Indianapolis, Indiana*

Copyright © 1978 by The Curtis Publishing Company. All rights reserved. No part of this book may be used or reproduced in any manner whatsoever without written permission except in the case of brief quotations embodied in critical articles and reviews. Printed in The United States of America. For information address The Curtis Publishing Company, Inc., 1100 Waterway Boulevard, Indianapolis, Indiana 46202. Library of Congress Catalog Card Number 78-61519. ISBN 0-89387-023-4.

THE CURTIS PUBLISHING COMPANY
*Chairman:* Beurt Ser Vaas
*President:* Cory Ser Vaas
*President Curtis Book Division:* Jack Merritt

*The Saturday Evening Post Book of the Sea and Ships*
*Editor:* Jean White
*Art Director and Designer:* Sandra Strother-Young
*Editorial Staff:* John J. Rea, Louise Fortson,
　John D. Craton, Sarah White
*Art Staff:* Jinny Sauer, Lucian Lupinski, Marianne Roan
*Compositors:* Penny Allison, Marie Caldwell,
　Gloria McCoy, Geri Watson

Other books in this series:
*The Saturday Evening Post Christmas Book*
*The Saturday Evening Post Movie Book*
*The Saturday Evening Post Norman Rockwell Book*
*The Saturday Evening Post Automobile Book*
*The Saturday Evening Post Animal Book*

DRAWN BY
SARAH S. STILWELL WEBER

The sea lies all around us. The commerce of all lands must cross it. The very winds that move over the lands have been cradled on its broad expanse and seek ever to return to it. The continents themselves dissolve and pass to the sea, in grain after grain of eroded land. . . . In its mysterious past it encompasses all the dim origins of life and receives in the end, after, it may be, many transmutations, the dead husks of that same life. For all at last returns to the sea—the beginning and the end.

RACHEL LOUISE CARSON

To me the sea is a continual miracle,
The fishes that swim—the rocks—the motion of the
    waves—the ships with men in them,
What stranger miracles are there?

WALT WHITMAN

I have seen old ships sail like swans asleep.

JAMES ELROY FLECKER

The sea is the land's edge also, the granite
Into which it reaches, the beaches where it tosses
Its hints of earlier and other creation:
The starfish, the hermit crab, the whale's backbone;
The pools where it offers to our curiosity
The more delicate algae and the sea anemone.
It tosses up our losses, the torn seine,
The shattered lobsterpot, the broken oar,
And the gear of foreign dead men. The sea
    has many voices.

THOMAS ELIOT

For boats, even the uglier ones, are among the loveliest creations of man's hands, and though owning them brings a train of debts, hangnails, bruises, bad frights, and all kinds of worries not experienced by those who content themselves with the more practical vices, the relation between a man and his boat is as personal and intimate as the relation between husband and wife.

DESMOND HOLDRIDGE

John Clymer

# Contents

## Sea Lore and Legends

## By Writers Who Went to Sea

# The Tall Ships

*Stories that appeared in the* Post *between 1948 and 1966 traced Horatio Hornblower's career from Midshipman to Admiral.*

# Hornblower and the Penalty of Failure

## A STORY BY C. S. FORESTER

Daylight crept over the tossing waters of the Bay of Biscay to reveal a small boat riding on its wide expanses. It was a very crowded boat; in the bows huddled the French crew of the sunken brig *Marie Galante*, amidships sat the captain and his mate, and in the sternsheets sat Midshipman Horatio Hornblower and the four English seamen who had once constituted the prize crew of the brig. Hornblower was seasick, for his delicate stomach, having just painfully accustomed itself to the motion of the *Indefatigable*, rebelled at the antics of the small boat as she pitched jerkily to her sea anchor. He was cold and weary as well as seasick after his second night without sleep—he had been vomiting spasmodically all through the hours of darkness, and in the depression which seasickness brings he had thought gloomily about the loss of the *Marie Galante*. If he had only remembered earlier to plug that shot hole! Excuses came to his mind only to be discarded. There had been so much to do, and so few men to do it with—the French crew to guard, the damage aloft to repair, the course to set. The absorbent qualities of the cargo of rice which the *Marie Galante* carried had deceived him when he had remembered to sound the well. All this might be true, but the fact remained that he had lost his ship, his first command. In his own eyes there was no excuse for his failure.

The French crew had wakened with the dawn and were chattering like a nest of magpies; Matthews and Carson beside him were moving stiffly to ease their aching joints.

"Breakfast, sir?" said Matthews.

It was like the games Hornblower had played as a lonely little boy, when he had sat in the empty pig trough and pretended he was cast away in an open boat.

Then he had parceled out the bit of bread or whatever it was which he had obtained from the kitchen into a dozen rations, counting them carefully, each one to last a day. But a small boy's eager appetite had made those days very short, not more than five minutes long; after standing up in the pig trough and shading his eyes and looking round the horizon for the succor that he could not discover, he would sit down again, tell himself that the life of a castaway was hard, and then decide that another night had passed and that it was time to eat another ration from his dwindling supply. So here under Hornblower's eye the French captain and mate served out a biscuit of hard bread to each person in the boat, and filled the pannikin for each man in turn from the water breakers under the thwarts. But Hornblower, when he sat in the pig trough, despite his vivid imagination, never thought of this hideous seasickness, of the cold and the cramps, nor of how his skinny posterior would ache because of constant pressure against the hard timbers of the sternsheets; nor, in the sublime self-confidence of childhood, had he ever thought how heavy could be the burden of responsibility on the shoulders of a senior naval officer aged 17.

He dragged himself back from the memories of that recent childhood to face the present situation. The gray sky, as far as his inexperienced eye could tell, bore no presage of deterioration in the weather. He wetted his finger and held it up, looking in the boat's compass to gauge the direction of the wind.

"Backing westerly a little, sir," said Matthews, who had been copying his movements.

"That's so," agreed Hornblower, hurriedly going through in his mind his recent lessons in boxing the compass. His course to weather Ushant was nor'east by north, he knew, and the boat close hauled would not lie closer than eight points off the wind—he had lain-to to the sea anchor all night because the wind had been coming from too far north to enable him to steer for England. But now the wind had backed. Eight points from nor'east by north was nor'west by west, and the wind was even more westerly than that. Close hauled he could weather Ushant and even have a margin for contingencies, to keep him clear of the lee shore which the seamanship books and his own common sense told him was so dangerous.

"We'll make sail, Matthews," he said; his hand was still grasping the biscuit which his rebellious stomach refused to accept.

"Aye aye, sir."

A shout to the Frenchmen crowded in the bows drew their attention; in the circumstances it hardly needed Hornblower's halting French to direct them to carry out the obvious task of getting in the sea anchor. But it was not too easy, with the boat so crowded and hardly a foot of freeboard. The mast was already stepped, and the lugsail bent ready to hoist. Two Frenchmen, balancing precariously, tailed onto the halyard and the sail rose up the mast.

"Hunter, take the sheet," said Hornblower. "Matthews, take the tiller. Keep her close hauled on the port tack."

"Close hauled on the port tack, sir."

The French captain had watched the proceedings with intense interest from his seat amidships. He had not understood the last, decisive order, but he grasped its meaning quickly enough when the boat came round and steadied on the port tack, heading for England. He stood up, spluttering angry protests.

"The wind is fair for Bordeaux," he said, gesticulating with clenched fists. "We could be there by tomorrow. Why do we go north?"

"We go to England," said Hornblower.

"But—but—it will take us a week! A week even if the wind stays fair. This boat—it is too crowded. We cannot endure a storm. It is madness."

Hornblower had guessed at the moment the captain stood up what he was going to say, and he hardly bothered to translate the expostulations to himself. He was too tired and too seasick to enter into an argument in a foreign language. He ignored the captain. Not for anything on earth would he turn the boat's head toward France. His naval career had only just begun, and even if it were to be blighted on account of the loss of the *Marie Galante* he had no intention of rotting for years in a French prison.

"Sir!" said the French captain.

The mate who shared the captain's thwart was protesting too, and now they turned to their crew behind them and told them what was going on. An angry movement stirred the crowd.

"Sir!" said the captain again. "I insist that you head toward Bordeaux."

He showed signs of advancing upon them; one of the crew behind him began to pull the boat hook clear, and it would be a dangerous weapon. Hornblower pulled one of the pistols from his belt and pointed it at the captain, who, with the muzzle four feet from his breast, fell back before the gesture. Without taking his eyes off him Hornblower took a second pistol with his left hand.

"Take this, Matthews," he said.

"Aye aye, sir," said Matthews, obeying, and then, after a respectful pause, "Beggin' your pardon, sir, but hadn't you better cock your pistol, sir?"

"Yes," said Hornblower, exasperated at his own forgetfulness.

He drew the hammer back with a click, and the menacing sound made more acute still the French captain's sense of his own danger, with a cocked and loaded pistol pointed at his stomach in a heaving boat. He waved his hands desperately.

"Please," he said, "point it some other way, sir."

He drew farther back, huddling against the men behind him.

"Hey, avast there, you," shouted Matthews loudly; a French sailor was trying to let go the halyard unobserved.

"Shoot any man who looks dangerous, Matthews," said Hornblower.

He was so intent on enforcing his will upon these men, so desperately anxious to retain his liberty, that his face was contracted into a beastlike scowl. No one looking at him could doubt his determination for a moment. He would allow no human life to come between him and his decisions. There was still a third pistol in his belt, and the Frenchmen could guess that if they tried a rush a quarter of them at least would meet their deaths before they overpowered the Englishmen, and the French captain knew he would be the first to die. His expressive hands, waving out from his sides—he could not take his eyes from the pistol—told his men to make no further resistance. Their murmurings died away, and the captain began to plead.

"Five years I was in an English prison during the last war," he said. "Let us reach an agreement. Let us go to France. When we reach the shore—anywhere you choose, sir—we will land and you can continue on your journey. Or we can all land, and I will use all my influence to have you and your men sent back to England under cartel, without exchange or ransom. I swear I will."

"No," said Hornblower.

England was far easier to reach from here than from the French Biscay coast; as for the other suggestion, Hornblower knew enough about the new government washed up by the revolution in France to be sure that they would never part with prisoners on the representation of a merchant captain. And trained seamen were scarce in France; it was his duty to keep these dozen from returning.

"No," he said again, in reply to the captain's fresh protests.

"Shall I clout 'im on the jaw, sir?" asked Hunter, at Hornblower's side.

"No," said Hornblower again, but the Frenchman saw the gesture and guessed at the meaning of the words, and subsided into sullen silence.

But he was roused again at the sight of Hornblower's pistol on his knee, still pointed at him. A sleepy finger might press that trigger.

"Sir," he said, "put that pistol away, I beg of you. It is dangerous."

Hornblower's eye was cold and unsympathetic.

"Put it away, please. I will do nothing to interfere with your command of this boat. I promise you that."

"Do you swear it?"

"I swear it."

"And these others?"

The captain looked round at his crew with voluble explanations, and grudgingly they agreed.

"They swear it too."

"Very well, then."

Hornblower started to replace the pistol in his belt, and remembered to put it on half-cock in time to save himself from shooting himself in the stomach. Everyone in the boat relaxed into apathy. The boat was rising and swooping rhythmically now, a far more comfortable motion than when it had jerked to a sea anchor, and Hornblower's stomach lost some of its resentment.

*"It was a very crowded boat...." A Hornblower illustration by Ken Riley.*

He had been two nights without sleep. His head lowered on his chest, and then he leaned sideways against Hunter, and slept peacefully, while the boat, with the wind nearly abeam, headed steadily for England. He was awakened late in the day when Matthews, cramped and weary, was compelled to surrender the tiller to Carson, and after that they kept watch and watch, a hand at the sheet and a hand at the tiller and the others trying to rest. Hornblower took his turn at the sheet, but he would not trust himself with the tiller, especially when night fell; he knew he had not the knack of keeping the boat on her course by the feel of the wind on his cheek and the tiller in his hand.

It was not until long after breakfast the next day—almost noon, in fact—that they sighted the sail. It was a Frenchman who saw it first, and his excited cry roused them all. There were three square topsails coming up over the horizon on their weather bow, nearing them so rapidly on a converging course that each time the boat rose on a wave a considerably greater area of canvas was visible.

"What do you think she is, Matthews?" asked Hornblower, while the boat buzzed with the Frenchmen's excitement.

"I can't tell, sir, but I don't like the looks of her," said Matthews doubtfully. "She ought to have her t'gallants set in this breeze—and her courses too, an' she hasn't. An' I don't like the cut of her jib, sir. She—she might be a Frenchie to me, sir."

Any ship traveling for peaceful purposes would naturally have all possible sail set. This ship had not. Hence she was engaged in some belligerent design, but still there were more chances that she was British than that she was French, even here in the Bay. Hornblower took a long look at her: a smallish vessel, although ship-rigged. Flush-decked, with a look of speed about her—her hull was visible at intervals now, with a line of gunports.

"She looks French all over to me, sir," said Hunter. "Privateer, seemly."

"Stand by to jibe," said Hornblower.

They brought the boat round before the wind, heading directly away from the ship. But in war as in the jungle, to fly is to invite pursuit and attack. The ship set

courses and topgallants and came tearing down upon them, passed them at half a cable's length and then hove-to, having cut off their escape. The ship's rail was lined with a curious crowd—a large crew for a vessel that size. A hail came across the water to the boat, and the words were French. The English seamen subsided into curses, while the French captain cheerfully stood up and replied, and the French crew brought the boat alongside the ship.

A handsome young man in a plum-colored coat with a lace stock greeted Hornblower when he stepped on the deck.

"Welcome, sir, to the *Pique*," he said in French. "I am Captain Neuville, of this privateer. And you are—?"

"Midshipman Hornblower, of His Britannic Majesty's Ship *Indefatigable*," growled Hornblower.

"You seem to be in an evil humor," said Neuville. "Please do not be so distressed at the fortunes of war. You will be accommodated in this ship, until we return to port, with every comfort possible at sea. I beg of you to consider yourself quite at home. For instance, those pistols in your belt must discommode you more than a little. Permit me to relieve you of their weight."

He took the pistols neatly from Hornblower's belt as he spoke, looked Hornblower keenly over, and then went on.

"That dirk that you wear at your side, sir. Would you oblige me by the loan of it? I assure you that I will return it to you when we part company. But while you are on board here I fear that your impetuous youth might lead you into some rash act while you are wearing a weapon which a credulous mind might believe to be lethal. A thousand thanks. And now might I show you the berth that is being prepared for you?"

With a courteous bow he led the way below. Two decks down, presumably at the level of a foot or two below the waterline, was a wide bare 'tween-decks, dimly lighted and scantily ventilated by the hatchways.

"Our slave deck," explained Neuville, carelessly.

"Slave deck?" asked Hornblower.

"Yes. It is here that the slaves were confined during the middle passage."

Much was clear to Hornblower at once. A slave ship could be readily converted into a privateer. She would already be armed with plenty of guns to defend herself against treacherous attacks while making her purchases in the African rivers; she was faster than the average merchant ship both because of the lack of need of hold space and because with a highly perishable cargo such as slaves speed was a desirable quality, and she was constructed to carry large numbers of men and the

great quantities of food and water necessary to keep them supplied while at sea in search of prizes.

"Our market in San Domingo has been closed to us by recent events, of which you must have heard, sir," went on Neuville, "and so that the *Pique* could continue to return dividends to me I have converted her into a privateer. Moreover, seeing that the activities of the Committee of Public Safety at present make Paris a more unhealthy spot even than the West Coast of Africa, I decided to take command of my vessel myself. To say nothing of the fact that a certain resolution and hardihood are necessary to make a privateer a profitable investment."

Neuville's face hardened for a moment into an expression of the grimmest determination, and then softened at once into its previous politeness.

"This door in this bulkhead," he continued, "leads to the quarters I have set aside for captured officers. Here, as you see, is your cot. Please make yourself at home here. Should this ship go into action—as I trust she will frequently do—the hatches above will be bat-

tened down. But except on those occasions you will of course be at liberty to move about the ship at your will. Yet I suppose I had better add that any harebrained attempt on the part of prisoners to interfere with the working or well-being of this ship would be deeply resented by the crew. They serve on shares, you understand, and are risking their lives and their liberty. I would not be surprised if any rash person who endangered their dividends and freedom were dropped over the side into the sea."

Hornblower forced himself to reply; he would not reveal that he was almost struck dumb by the calculating callousness of this last speech.

"I understand," he said.

"Excellent! Now is there anything further you may need, sir?"

Hornblower looked round the bare quarters in which he was to suffer lonely confinement, lit by a dim glimmer of light from a swaying slush lamp.

"Could I have something to read?" he asked.

Neuville thought for a moment.

*"She had been damaged by gunfire before surrendering." By Anton Otto Fischer.*

"I fear there are only professional books," he said. "But I can let you have Grandjean's *Principles of Navigation* and Lebrun's *Handbook on Seamanship* and some similar volumes, if you think you can understand the French in which they are written."

"I'll try," said Hornblower.

Probably it was as well that Hornblower was provided with the materials for such strenuous mental exercise. The effort of reading French and of studying his profession at one and the same time kept his mind busy during the dreary days while the *Pique* cruised in search of prizes. Most of the time the Frenchmen ignored him—he had to force himself upon Neuville once to protest against the employment of his four British seamen on the menial work of pumping out the ship, but he had to retire worsted from the argument, if argument it could be called, when Neuville icily refused to discuss the question. Hornblower went back to his quarters with burning cheeks and red ears, and, as ever, when he was mentally disturbed, the thought of his guilt returned to him with new force.

If only he had plugged that shot hole sooner! A clearer-headed officer, he told himself, would have done so. He had lost his ship, the *Indefatigable*'s precious prize, and there was no health in him. Sometimes he made himself review the situation calmly. Professionally, he might not—probably would not—suffer for his negligence. A midshipman with only four for a prize crew, put on board a 200-ton brig that had been subjected to considerable firing from a frigate's guns, would not be seriously blamed when she sank under him. But Hornblower knew at the same time that he was at least partly at fault. If it was ignorance—there was no excuse for ignorance. If he had allowed his multiple cares to distract him from the business of plugging the shot hole immediately, that was incompetence, and there was no excuse for incompetence. When he thought along those lines he was overwhelmed by waves of despair and of self-contempt, and there was no one to comfort him. The day of his birthday, when he looked at himself at the vast age of 18, was the worst of all. Eighteen and a discredited prisoner in the hands of a French privateersman! His self-respect was at its lowest ebb.

The *Pique* was seeking her prey in the most frequented waters in the world, the approaches to the Channel, and there could be no more vivid demonstration of the vastness of the ocean than the fact that she cruised day after day without glimpsing a sail. She maintained a triangular course, reaching to the northwest, tacking to the south, running under easy sail northeasterly again,

with lookouts at every masthead, with nothing to see but the tossing waste of water—until the morning when a high-pitched yell from the fore topgallant masthead attracted the attention of everybody on deck, including Hornblower, standing lonely in the waist. Neuville, by the wheel, bellowed a question to the lookout, and Hornblower, thanks to his recent studies, could translate the answer. There was a sail visible to windward, and next moment the lookout reported that it had altered course and was running down toward them.

That meant a great deal. In wartime any merchant ship would be suspicious of strangers and would give them as wide a berth as possible; and especially when she was to windward and therefore far safer. Only someone prepared to fight or possessed of a perfectly morbid curiosity would abandon a windward position. A wild and unreasonable hope filled Hornblower's breast; a ship of war at sea—thanks to England's maritime mastery—would be far more probably English than French. And this was the cruising ground of the *Indefatigable*, his own ship, stationed there specially to fulfill the double function of looking out for French commerce-destroyers and intercepting French blockade-runners. A hundred miles from here she had put him and his prize crew on board the *Marie Galante*. It was a thousand to one, he exaggerated despairingly to himself, against any ship sighted being the *Indefatigable.* But—hope reasserted itself—the fact that she was coming down to investigate reduced the odds to ten to one at most. Less than ten to one.

He looked over at Neuville, trying to think his thoughts. The *Pique* was fast and handy, and there was a clear avenue of escape to leeward. The fact that the stranger had altered course toward them was a suspicious circumstance, but it was known that Indiamen, the richest prizes of all, had sometimes traded on the similarity of their appearance to that of ships of the line, and, by showing a bold front, had scared dangerous enemies away. That would be a temptation to a man eager to make a prize. At Neuville's orders all sail was set, ready for instant flight or pursuit, and, close-hauled, the *Pique* stood toward the stranger. It was not long before Hornblower, on deck, caught a glimpse of a gleam of white, like a tiny grain of rice, far away on the horizon as the *Pique* lifted on a swell. Here came Matthews, red-faced and excited, running aft to Hornblower's side.

"That's the old *Indefatigable,* sir," he said. "I swear it!"

He sprang onto the rail, holding on by the shrouds, and stared under his hand.

"Yes! There she is, sir! She's loosing her royals now, sir. We'll be back on board of her in time for grog!"

A French petty officer reached up and dragged Matthews by the seat of his trousers from his perch, and with a blow and a kick drove him forward again, while a moment later Neuville was shouting the orders that wore the ship round to head away directly from the *Indefatigable*. Neuville beckoned Hornblower over to his side.

"Your late ship, I understand, Mr. Hornblower?"

"Yes."

"What is her best point of sailing?"

Hornblower's eyes met Neuville's.

"Do not look so noble," said Neuville, smiling with thin lips. "I could undoubtedly induce you to give me the information. I know of ways. But it is unnecessary, fortunately for you. There is no ship on earth—especially none of His Britannic Majesty's clumsy frigates—that can outsail the *Pique* running before the wind. You will soon see that."

He strolled to the taffrail and looked aft long and earnestly through his glass, but no more earnestly than did Hornblower with his naked eye.

"You see?" said Neuville, proffering the glass.

Hornblower took it, but more to catch a closer glimpse of his ship than to confirm his observations. He was homesick, desperately homesick, at that moment, for the *Indefatigable*. But there could be no denying that she was being left fast behind. Her topgallants were out of sight again now, and only her royals were visible.

"Two hours and we shall have run her mastheads under," said Neuville, taking back the telescope and shutting it with a snap.

He left Hornblower standing sorrowful at the taffrail while he turned to berate the helmsman for not steering a steadier course; Hornblower heard the explosive words without listening to them, the wind blowing into his face and ruffling his hair over his ears, and the wake

of the ship's passage boiling below him. So might Adam have looked back at Eden; Hornblower remembered the stuffy dark midshipman's berth, the smells and the creakings, the bitter cold nights, turning out in response to the call for all hands, the weevily bread and the wooden beef, and he yearned for them all, with the sick feeling of hopeless longing. Liberty was vanishing over the horizon. Yet it was not these personal feelings that drove him below in search of action. They may have quickened his wits, but it was a sense of duty which inspired him.

The slave deck was deserted as usual, with all hands at quarters. Beyond the bulkhead stood his cot with the books upon it and the slush lamp swaying above it. There was nothing there to give him any inspiration. There was another locked door in the after bulkhead. That opened into some kind of boatswain's store; twice he had seen it unlocked and paint and similar supplies brought out from it. Paint! That gave him an idea; he looked from the door up to the slush lamp and back again, and as he stepped forward he took his claspknife out of his pocket. But before very long he recoiled again, sneering at himself. The door was not paneled, but was made of two solid slabs of wood, with the crossbeams on the inside. There was the keyhole of the lock, but it presented no point of attack. It would take him hours and hours to cut through that door with his knife, at a time when minutes were precious.

His heart was beating feverishly—but no more feverishly than his mind was working—as he looked round again. He reached up to the lamp and shook it; nearly full. There was a moment when he stood hesitating, nerving himself, and then he threw himself into action. With a ruthless hand he tore the pages out of Grandjean's *Principes de la Navigation,* crumpling them up in small quantities into little loose balls, which he laid at the foot of the door. He threw off his uniform coat and dragged his blue woolen jersey over his head; his long powerful fingers tore it across and plucked eagerly at it to unravel it. After starting some loose threads he would not waste more time on it, and dropped the garment onto the paper and looked round again. The mattress of the cot! It was stuffed with straw, by God! A slash of his knife tore open the ticking, and he scooped the stuff out by the armful; constant pressure had almost solidified it, but he shook it and handled it so that it bulked out far larger in a mass on the deck nearly up to his waist. That would give him the intense blaze he wanted. He stood still, compelling himself to think clearly and logically—it was impetuosity and lack of thought which had occasioned the loss of the *Marie*

*"There is no ship on earth . . . that can outsail the* Pique *running before the wind. You will soon see that."*

Galante, and now he had wasted time on his jersey. He worked out the successive steps to take. He made a long spill out of a page of the *Manuel de Matelotage,* and lighted it at the lamp. Then he poured out the grease—the lamp was hot and the grease liquid—over his balls of paper, over the deck, over the base of the door. A touch from his taper lighted one ball, the flame traveled quickly. He was committed now. He piled the straw upon the flames, and in a sudden access of insane strength he tore the cot from its fastenings, smashing it as he did so, and piled the fragments on the straw.

Already the flames were racing through the straw. He dropped the lamp upon the pile, grabbed his coat, and walked out. He thought of closing the door, but decided against it—the more air the better. He wriggled into his coat and ran up the ladder.

On deck he forced himself to lounge nonchalantly against the rail, putting his shaking hands into his pockets. His excitement made him weak, nor was it lessened as he waited. Every minute before the fire could be discovered was important. A French officer said something to him with a triumphant laugh and

*"Hornblower, looking forward, saw the* Indefatigable *again. She was tearing down toward them will all sails set."*

pointed aft over the taffrail, presumably speaking about leaving the *Indefatigable* behind. Hornblower smiled bleakly at him; that was the first gesture that occurred to him, and then he tought that a smile was out of place, and he tried to assume a sullen scowl. The wind was blowing briskly, so that the *Pique* could only just carry all plain sail; Hornblower felt it on his cheeks, which were burning. Everyone on deck seemed unnaturally busy and preoccupied; Neuville was watching the helmsman with occasional glances aloft to see that every sail was doing its work; the men were at the guns, two hands and a petty officer heaving the log. God, how much longer would he have?

Look there! The coaming of the after hatchway appeared distorted, wavering in the shimmering air. Hot air must be coming up through it. And was that, or was it not, the ghost of a wreath of smoke? It was! In

that moment the alarm was given. A loud cry, a rush of feet, an instant bustle, the loud beating of a drum, highpitched shouts—*"Au feu! Au feu!"*

The four elements of Aristotle, thought Hornblower, insanely, earth, air, water, and fire, were the constant enemies of the seaman, but the lee shore, the gale, and the wave, were none of them as feared in wooden ships as fire. Timbers many years old, and coated thick with paint, burnt fiercely and readily. Sails and tarry rigging would burn like fireworks. And within the ship there were tons and tons of gunpowder waiting its chance to blast the ship and the seaman into fragments.

Hornblower watched the fire parties flinging themselves into their work, the pumps being dragged over the decks, the hoses rigged. Someone came racing aft with a message for Neuville, presumably to report the site of the fire. Neuville heard him, and darted a glance at Hornblower against the rail before he hurled orders back at the messenger. The smoke coming up through the after hatchway was dense now; at Neuville's orders the afterguard flung themselves down the opening through the smoke. And there was more smoke, and more smoke; smoke caught up by the following wind and blown forward in wisps—smoke must be pouring out of the sides of the ship at the waterline.

Neuville took a stride toward Hornblower, his face working with rage, but a cry from the helmsman checked him. The helmsman, unable to take his hands from the wheel, pointed with his foot to the cabin skylight. There was a flickering of flame below it. A side pane fell in as they watched, and a rush of flame came through the opening. That store of paint, Hornblower calculated—he was calmer now, with a calm that would astonish him later, when he came to look back on it—must be immediately under the cabin, and blazing fiercely. Neuville looked round him, at the sea and the sky, and put his hands to his head in a furious gesture. For the first time in his life Hornblower saw a man literally tearing his hair. But his nerve held.

A shout brought up another portable pump; four men set to work on the handles, and the clank-clank, clank-clank made an accompaniment that blended with the roar of the fire. A thin jet of water was squirted down the gaping skylight. More men formed a bucket chain, drawing water from the sea and passing it from hand to hand to pour in the skylight, but those buckets of water were less effective even than the stream from the pumps. From below came the dull thud of an explosion, and Hornblower caught his breath as he expected the ship to be blown to pieces. But no further explosion followed; either a gun had been set off by the flames or a cask had burst violently in the heat. And then the bucket line suddenly disintegrated; beneath the feet of one of the men a seam had gaped in a broad red smile from which came a rush of flame. Some officer had seized Neuville by the arm, and was arguing with him vehemently, and Hornblower could see Neuville yield in despair. Hands went scurrying aloft to get in the fore topsail and forecourse, and other hands went to the main braces. Over went the wheel, and the *Pique* came up into the wind.

The change was dramatic, although at first more apparent than real; with the wind blowing in the opposite direction the roar of the fire did not come so clearly to the ears of those forward of it. But it was an immense gain, all the same; the flames, which had started in the steerage in the farthest after part of the ship, no longer

were blown forward, but were turned back upon timber already half consumed. Yet the after part of the deck was fully alight; the helmsman was driven from the wheel, and in a flash the flames took hold of the driver and consumed it utterly—one moment the sail was there, and the next there were only charred fragments hanging from the gaff. But, head to wind, the other sails did not catch and a mizzen trysail hurriedly set kept the ship bows on.

It was then that Hornblower, looking forward, saw the *Indefatigable* again. She was tearing down toward them with all sails set; as the *Pique* lifted he could see the white bow wave foaming under her bowsprit. There was no question about surrender, for under the menace of that row of guns no ship of the *Pique*'s force, even if uninjured, could resist. A cable's length to windward the *Indefatigable* rounded-to, and she was hoisting out her boats before even she was fully round. Pellew had seen the smoke, and had deduced the reason for the *Pique*'s heaving-to, and had made his preparations as he came up. Longboat and launch had each a pump in their bows where sometimes they carried a carronade; they dropped down to the stern of the *Pique* to cast their jets of water up into the flaming stern without more ado. Two gigs full of men ran straight aft to join in

"FOR THE FREEDOM OF THE SEA, BY CYRUS TOWNSEND BRADY (*See Page 399*)
*'She was hoisting out her boats before she was fully round.'* On these two pages, 1899 Post *covers by George Gibbs.*

the battle with the flames, but Bolton, the third lieutenant, lingered for a moment as he caught Hornblower's eye.

"Good God, it's you!" he exclaimed. "What are you doing here?"

Yet he did not stay for an answer. He picked out Neuville as the captain of the *Pique*, strode aft to receive his surrender, cast his eyes aloft to see that all was well there, and then took up the task of combating the fire. The flames were overcome in time, more because they had consumed everything within reach of them than for any other reason; the *Pique* was burnt from the taffrail forward for some feet of her length right to the water's edge, so that she presented a strange spectacle when viewed from the deck of the *Indefatiga-*

*Hornblower ashore, by Ken Riley.*

*ble*. Nevertheless, she was in no immediate danger; given even moderate good fortune and a little hard work she could be sailed to England to be repaired and sent to sea again.

But it was not her salvage that was important, but rather the fact that she was no longer in French hands, would no longer be available to prey on English commerce. That was the point that Sir Edward Pellew made in conversation with Hornblower, when the latter came on board to report himself.

Hornblower had begun, at Pellew's order, by recounting what had happened to him from the time he had been sent as prize master on board the *Marie Galante*. As Hornblower had expected—perhaps as he had even feared—Pellew had passed lightly over the loss of the brig. She had been damaged by gunfire before surrendering, and no one now could establish whether the damage was small or great. Pellew did not give the matter a second thought. Hornblower had tried to save her and had been unsuccessful with his tiny crew—and at that moment the *Indefatigable* could not spare him a larger crew. He did not hold Hornblower culpable. Once again, it was more important that France should be deprived of the *Marie Galante*'s cargo than that England should benefit by it. The situation was exactly parallel to that of the salvaging of the *Pique*.

"It was lucky she caught fire like that," commented Pellew, looking across to where the *Pique* lay, still hove-to with the boats clustering about her but with only the thinnest trail of smoke drifting from her stern. "She was running clean away from us, and would have been out of sight in an hour. Have you any idea how it happened, Mr. Hornblower?"

Hornblower was naturally expecting that question and was ready for it.

Now was the time to answer truthfully and modestly, to receive the praise he deserved, a mention in the *Gazette*, perhaps even appointment as acting-lieutenant. But Pellew did not know the full details of the loss of the brig, and might make a false estimate of them even if he did.

"No, sir," said Hornblower. "I think it must have been spontaneous combustion in that paint locker. I can't account for it otherwise."

He alone knew of his remissness in plugging that shot hole, he alone could decide on his punishment, and this was what he had chosen. This alone could re-establish him in his own eyes, and when the words were spoken he felt enormous relief, and not one single twinge of regret.

"It was fortunate, all the same," mused Pellew.

*Captain McIntyre was lucky—he became captain of a rich man's sailing yacht. A 1901 cover design, artist unknown.*

# Farewell to the Windbags

## BY CAPTAIN OREN F. McINTYRE

The age of sail was dead when I was born. I did not know it, or else I refused to believe it. It was in my blood. Since 1632, at least, the men of my family had been seamen. In 1899, when I was born in New Harbor, Maine, my father was reduced to captain of an old schooner freighting rock and lime. When I was eight, he called quits and moved to Portland to run a coal-and-wood yard.

I was drawn to the docks as modern boys to an airport or the movies. Sails were not uncommon yet in Portland harbor and, large or small, smart or slack, I sailed them all in imagination, saw myself fisting in a slamming topsail in a breeze, or at the wheel of a clipper in the long swells off Cape Stiff. I mooned like a lover at the taper of the spars, the saucy angle of the thrusting jibboom, the seductive sweep of the low deck; knew every block, rope, wire, and chain and, daydreaming, would overstay my leave and take my punishment stoically. A little older, I made my way aboard and was driven off by swearing crews. Then, at 12, I went aboard to stay, apprenticed to a dead trade.

It was a rock coaster, a schooner trudging granite from Maine ports, such a one as had been my father's last command. "Captain, sir," I piped, cap in hand, "could you use a man like me? I love ships and can go aloft and make a topsail fast real quick."

"Did you ever do it?" he asked dryly.

Well, no, I hadn't actually done it, but only for lack of opportunity. I talked fast. My father? He wouldn't care; it even was his ambition that his son succeed him on the sea, I protested. I would bring him down, or a letter from him. Privately, I made up my mind, if my father refused, to hire with my two dollars' savings a foster father from among the waterfront loafers. There were tears in my eyes and the captain gave in. My father didn't give in so easily.

These rock coasters carried granite below and above decks until they were awash amidships, so they scurried from cover to cover and watched the weather nervously. Their usual crew was a captain, a mate, a cook, a sailor, and a boy. The topsails were light and a boy could save older legs. The food was poor, the hours long, the life hard, but I was on the way to be a sailor. What time I wasn't running aloft I helped splice the old

ropes, patch her worn canvas, and jumped when spoken to. In return, they paid me a dollar now and then, and took an interest in teaching me the trade. I stayed seven months and quit of wounded dignity. The skipper was one who would walk the poop, curse, rage, and shake his fists at heaven when head winds blew. In such a temper, and through no fault of mine, he kicked me. I threw a sheath knife at him, cutting a gash in his cheek, and shipped as boy on another rock coaster. Except the first year, I went to school in winter, sailed in summer, and graduated at 15 to a full hand at $20 a month on a Maine three-masted schooner. Since then I have been a seaman in the Navy during the war, a mate in steam, mate and captain in sail with a master-for-all-oceans ticket. Now, at 32, I command a schooner yacht. Fortunately, of the 3,500 yachts now flying the American flag, about one in three are sail, and many of these are owned by sportsmen and manned by hired crews.

As short a time ago as 1926, Crowley & Thurlow of Boston, for one, operated some 40 sailing ships in cargo trades. They operate none now. Not more than half a dozen sailing cargo vessels are left on the Atlantic Coast, few more on the Pacific. They existed for years on the steamers' leavings. Cutting every cost corner, running without insurance, they still could pick up a cargo when speed and certainty did not count, but with the seas glutted with steamers and motor ships, ocean freights less than in 1913, the gulls are picking the bones of the old and neglected windbags.

The last great gathering of the sails was at Miami in the winter of 1925-26, at the height of the Florida boom. With the East Coast Railroad choked with freight and an embargo declared, every hull that still held together was dragged off the mud and loaded with building materials. Around 50 windjammers lay outside at anchor awaiting berths while an equal number were discharging in the harbor. No such fleet ever will meet again.

*Some sailing ships died slowly, of rust and rot, becalmed in tropic ports where there were no cargoes for them.*

*Other ships met a quick death at the hands of wreckers. By 1931, when Captain McIntyre wrote this article, almost all were gone.*

# The Tall Ships Today

They don't go to sea any longer, except now and then when they have to be towed away from their docks for one reason or another; but they are alive and well.

The wind sings in their taut rigging. Their decks are scrubbed, their brightwork polished, their hulls freshly painted. Pennants fly at the mastheads. All wooden parts are inspected regularly and the timbers replaced, one at a time, when there is decay.

They are the sailing ships that survived their own obsolescence. Rescued, restored, and repaired, they are now treasured memorials to a glorious past—and wonderful places to visit.

The most famous of the restored ships, one visited by almost every family making a summer pilgrimage to the historic shrines of New England, is the U.S.S. *Constitution*, docked in the Charles River near Boston. She was built in Boston, 1794-1797, to be the greatest of all fighting ships, able to outsail and outgun any vessel, and to outrun any superior force she dared not attack. She had a longer, deeper hull than other frigates of the time, and a greater spread of sail. She earned her nickname, "Old Ironsides," when shots from the British warship *Guerrière* bounced harmlessly off her two-

*Visitors to the* Charles W. Morgan *at Mystic Seaport can watch men climb the rigging, then set or furl the sails.*

foot-thick solid oak hull. The *Constitution* was on active service with the U.S. Navy until 1860, when she was retired to serve as a training ship and later, with masts removed and deck roofed over, as a receiving center for recruits.

Pennies collected by schoolchildren helped to finance the first restoration of the *Constitution*, completed in 1906. Since then she has been a floating museum. Tourists stand in line to board her on summer weekends, and the annual turning of the ship in the Boston Harbor, so that she will weather evenly on her two sides, draws crowds of observers. A salute is fired, cheers sound from the small boats that form an escort, and photographers snap hundreds of pictures.

A sister ship, the U.S.S. *Constellation*, may be visited at her dock in Baltimore, Maryland. Smaller than the *Constitution* and built a few years later in Baltimore, she is honored as the first U.S. warship to capture an enemy vessel. She was restored in the early '60s and declared a National Historic Monument in 1964.

At Mystic Seaport in Connecticut one can visit the *Charles W. Morgan*, a wooden whaling ship built in 1841 that is the last of her kind. She sailed for more than 80 years and the whales her boats harpooned earned more than $1,400,000 for her owners. Whalers

*Small boats follow the* Constitution *on her annual voyage out into Boston Harbor where she is turned around.*

*The* Balclutha *is on display at San Francisco.*

*The* Falls of Clyde *is docked at Honolulu.*

were blunt, square ships, built for work rather than for speed. They were home to 20 or 30 men for the duration of a whaling expedition, which could last up to four years, and they were also factories where the whales were processed to obtain the valuable oil, whalebone, and ambergris.

Retired from whaling in 1921, the *Charles W. Morgan* was featured in two movies of the '20s, and was nearly destroyed by the hurricane of 1938. Mystic Seaport acquired her in 1941, and in 1967 she was formally designated a National Historic Landmark.

At Mystic Seaport one can also go aboard the *Joseph Conrad*, a small-scale full-rigged ship built in Denmark in 1882 to serve as a training ship and a fishing schooner.

On the West Coast, the San Francisco Maritime Museum features a restored ship with an interesting history.

The *Balclutha* was launched in Scotland in 1886. She followed the Pacific sea lanes until 1902, rounding Cape Horn 17 times. In 1902 she went to work for the salmon trade, transporting fishermen, cannery hands, and supplies to Alaska, returning with thousands of cases of canned salmon. On one of these voyages she ran aground near Kodiak Island. She was considered a total wreck, but one of her owners had faith in her and managed to get the *Balclutha* back to San Francisco, repair her, and put her back to work. She continued in service to the salmon trade until 1930.

Then her career changed radically. A carnival promoter bought the *Balclutha*, painted her silver, with red masts and spars, and hung wax figures of mutineers from her yardarms. She traveled the ports of the West Coast in this undignified manner; then she, too, went into movies. The *Balclutha* appeared in *Mutiny on the Bounty* with Clark Gable, even though the *Bounty* was an 18th-century wooden ship and the *Balclutha* was 19th-century and made of steel.

Karl Kortum, now director of the San Francisco Maritime Museum, spearheaded the effort to acquire the ship and restore her as a museum piece, work that was done entirely with volunteer help and funds. Local labor unions contributed free labor, mostly on weekends, while businessmen contributed materials and money. Even the coffee drunk by the workmen was contributed. The *Balclutha* now earns around $100,000 a year as a tourist attraction, providing for her own upkeep in the years to come.

In Hawaii another sail merchantman is being restored. She is the *Falls of Clyde*, docked at the Bishop Museum in Honolulu. Built in Scotland in 1878, the

*Anton Otto Fischer painted the* Cutty Sark *under full sail in a sea full of dolphins for the* Post *in 1933.*

*Falls of Clyde* served first in the Indian trade. After 1907 she carried oil and molasses between Hawaii and San Francisco. Her last trip under sail was in 1921. With masts removed, she served another 35 years as a floating service station off Alaska, dispensing oil to fishing boats. She was slated for wrecking in 1959 when William Mitchell, who recognized the beautiful lines of her still sound hull, arranged to have her towed to Seattle. Honolulu schoolchildren helped raise the money to have her returned to Hawaii for restoration and display.

In England one may visit two restored ships that are very different though each is beautiful and of great historical interest.

The clipper ship *Cutty Sark*, docked at Greenwich,

looks very familiar to Americans who have seen her picture on labels and advertisements. She was built in 1870 as a tea clipper—one of the highly specialized ships designed to race from China to England, where tea from the first ship to arrive would bring a premium price. *Cutty Sark* once made the run in 107 days.

The great day of the tea clipper was brief, because of the development of steamships and increased use of the Suez Canal. In 1883 the *Cutty Sark* entered the Australian wool trade and set speed records that still stand. On one trip she outran the mail steamer *Britannia*, then considered the fastest ship in the world. *Cutty Sark* carried miscellaneous cargoes around the Atlantic for a quarter of a century, was nearly destroyed by storms, then served as a training ship through World War II. Prince Philip, Duke of Edinburgh, was influential in having her restored as a museum, and in 1957 Queen Elizabeth opened the ship to the public.

In Scottish dialect a "cutty sark" is a short nightgown, usually worn by a prostitute. In a poem by Robert Burns, Tam O'Shanter is chased by a witch wearing a cutty sark. The name seems an odd one to be

*The most colorful of the restored ships, the H.M.S.* Victory *is striped yellow and black, with accents of red and gold.*

*The tallest of the restored ships, the* Cutty Sark *carried 32,000 square feet of canvas on her towering masts.*

chosen by a conservative Scottish sea captain but it proved a lucky one. The ship's figurehead is a witch wearing a cutty sark, and her wind vane is shaped like a short nightgown.

H.M.S. *Victory*, Admiral Nelson's flagship that led the British fleet into the battle of Trafalgar, is docked at Portsmouth. She was damaged by enemy fire for the first time in 1778, and for the last time in 1941, when a German bomb fell between her hull and the side of her drydock. Her keel was laid in 1759, but she was not completed until 1765. H.M.S. *Victory* is an authentic relic of the British Navy that boasted of "wooden ships and iron men"; she was built to be a flagship and she still serves as flagship of the Naval Home Command in Portsmouth.

Aboard her, one sees the brocade-covered swinging bed in which Admiral Nelson slept, and the wardroom where the officers took their meals in spacious comfort. Below, in low-ceilinged 'tweendecks space, the seaman's hammocks are swung over and around the ship's guns; their wooden messkits are on the tables. On deck, an engraved plate marks the spot where Nelson fell on October 21, 1805.

The restored sailing ships are living ships and living history; while they survive, the great day of Tall Ships will not be forgotten.

The Edge
of the
Sea

# The Snowflake and the Starfish

## A STORY BY ROBERT NATHAN

The sea witch came in on the tide, riding on the waves like foam, and her hair floated out behind her like seaweed. She came to the beach and lay there breathing slightly, and her eyes searched everywhere like a hungry gull. And Michael Doyle's little daughter, Vicky, walking along the beach in search of colored shells, turned to her brother, Little Thomas, and said, "It's time we went home to supper."

"I think I saw something behind those rocks," said Little Thomas.

"All right," said Vicky, "do you want to go and look?"

"No," said Little Thomas.

The two children turned and started home down the beach; and the sea witch lowered herself gently into the water and swam quietly along the shore, halfway out, keeping an eye on them, and now and then diving through the waves like a porpoise. She was lonely; she had no children of her own to play with.

Vicky and her brother Little Thomas lived in a house close to the water with their father Michael Doyle, the professor, and his wife Helen. It was a good place for playing or looking for shells, except in winter, when the fogs came in or when it rained. Then they stayed indoors or walked on the hills above the sea in the weedy grass and looked down at the ocean, gray and cold and lonely everywhere.

But now it was summer, and they went almost every day to the beach. They knew that there were many strange things in the sea, some of which they wouldn't like; but they were mostly far out where they would never bother ordinary people, like the giant octopus that lived far down in the deep dark bottom of the ocean somewhere on the way to China.

But the things that were nearer at hand they knew very well. They knew the sea gulls and the little sand crabs who lived there, and the hermit crabs in their shells, and the quick, darting sandpipers; and they knew the fishermen who came there to spin their lines out over the surf and stand patient and still until it was time to reel their lines in again. Or sometimes a skin diver would clump down to the water in his big rubber fins and put on his mask and go sliding out to sea like a seal, pushing a blown-up rubber tube in front of him.

Their mother was very kind to them and sewed Little Thomas' buttons on when they came off, and often gave Vicky pennies to put in her hope chest, which was an earthenware bank in the shape of a pig. Vicky loved to hear it jingle when she shook it. She thought that someday when she was grown up she would be able to buy anything she wanted in the world for three or four dollars. She didn't know exactly what it would be. Mrs. Doyle thought that with a hope chest it would be nice to buy silver spoons or linen pillowcases, but that wasn't what Vicky wanted at all. What she wanted was——

And there she stopped, because she wasn't sure what it was she wanted.

"Why," asked her father, who was a professor at the university, "don't you buy yourself a nice dictionary, or a small encyclopedia?" And he wrinkled up his nose and nodded his head and knocked the ashes out of his pipe.

"A little learning never did anybody any harm."

But Vicky shook her head; that wasn't what she wanted either. What she wanted was something beautiful and strange, not everyday. Something different—something that nobody else had.

That night as they were getting ready for bed she said to her brother Little Thomas, "What do you want most in all the world?"

Little Thomas bounced up and down in his bed once or twice before settling down for the night. "I guess I

*A summery sea goddess by E. M. Jackson graced the* Post *in 1927. Like the witch in the story, she comes "riding on the waves like foam."*

got everything I want," he said, "or almost. What I want is a private snake."

Vicky lay back with a sigh and looked up at the ceiling. Her brother's answer was no help to her. Little boys always seemed satisfied with something ordinary, whereas little girls always had to look for something curious and rare. A secret treasure that nobody else knew about, a strangeness, a difference—a little moon to wear in her hair, a star of her own, a personal snowflake. They were such lovely dreams. That was what a hope chest was for: to hold dreams. That was why boys didn't have them.

Outside in the dim blue night the sea witch lay on the sand near the Doyle house and sang a sad sea song and wept a little. Neither of the children heard her.

*A secret treasure,* thought Vicky drowsily. *A star of my own, a snowflake for my cheek.*

"*Empty is the sea,*" sang the sea witch, "*and the shore empty—*"

The children slept, and the sea witch stirred a little and began to weave her spell. "Sea porcupine," she whispered, "sea anemone; crab, oyster, kelp, plankton, barnacle, clam, abalone—like a snail, quiet, blind, creep into a girl's mind. Find among her little pleasures what she treasures here below. Herring, sturgeon, pompano, little octopus, and squid, creep along, safely hid; where a child lies asleep, creep, creep. Halibut and sea trout, what do children dream about?"

But the spell missed Vicky, for whom it was intended, and crept like a little gray fog around Little Thomas' bed instead. And the sea witch drew back in surprise.

"A private snake?" she exclaimed. "How odd."

She thought a moment. "Something has gone wrong," she declared. "There has been some mistake. Abalone! Pompano! Try again."

This time the spell worked properly, and then the sea witch knew what she wanted to know.

Next morning when the children woke up there was a tiny, silvery starfish lying at the foot of Vicky's bed, and on Little Thomas' counterpane there was a small stuffed eel.

"I declare," said Mrs. Doyle, sweeping them out-of-doors, "how a person is to keep her house in order, I don't know."

Vicky and Little Thomas looked at each other. "But mother," said Vicky, "it wasn't us."

"I suppose they walked in by themselves," said Mrs. Doyle.

"Leptocephalus conger," said Michael Doyle, the professor, "minor, and Asterias rubens. They couldn't

have walked in by themselves, my dear. Besides they were quite dead."

"See," said Little Thomas. "I told you."

"Woman's work is never done," said Mrs. Doyle with a sigh.

Because it was a lovely warm day, the two children went down to play on the beach, and as they were playing there in the bright sunny foam, the sea witch looked out of a wave and saw them.

Her feelings had been hurt at seeing her gifts swept out with scraps of paper, old bottle caps, bits of string, and a stocking with a hole in it; and it was some time before she could bring herself to speak to them. At last, however, when it was almost time for lunch, she took a deep breath and came out of the water onto the sand, dressed in striped bombazine for all the world like somebody's nurse.

"Well," she said, "hello, there."

Vicky looked at her in surprise. What a strange thing for somebody's nurse to say, she thought: "Hello, there." They usually said things like, "How do you do, little children?" or, "Har-rum." Come to think of it, she didn't look very much like a nurse, either—with her sad face and her sea-colored eyes and her long hair with seaweed in it.

As a matter of fact, the sea witch didn't know how to talk to children at all. "I know a secret," she said. "Do you?"

"No," said Little Thomas. "And if I did," he added, "I wouldn't tell you."

The sea witch drew back with a hurt look. "Sticks and stones can break my bones," she said, "but words can never hurt me.

"That isn't true," she said a moment later, because she was honest; "words are full of power to harm and to heal. Like 'hateful,' which is like a stick for beating; and 'lovely,' which melts in your mouth like oysters."

"Oysters don't melt in your mouth," said Vicky. "They just sit there till you swallow them."

"What I really meant," said the sea witch in a far-away voice, "was marzipan."

"Marzipan is what witches eat," said Vicky and, rising to her feet, she said to Little Thomas, "I think I hear our mother calling us. She wants us to come home for lunch."

Little Thomas rose obediently, and the two children went back to their house, not looking over their shoulders, holding their breath and being very careful to walk withershins around the piles of seaweed lying on the sand.

Nevertheless, Little Thomas had forgotten his pail

*"It was a good place for playing or looking for shells."* This beach is near Lapash, Washington; the 1957 Post *cover is by John Clymer.*

and shovel; and these, with a sly smile, the sea witch took back with her to her cave in the rocks. It was very important to have something belonging to one of the children if she ever hoped to gain power over them.

And besides, the pail smelled of little boys playing in the sand in the sun, and that was a comfort to her.

That afternoon Vicky and Little Thomas stayed home and played quietly in their room. It puzzled Mrs. Doyle that they didn't seem to want to go out. "It's such a lovely day," she said. "Don't you want to go down and play on the beach some more?"

"No," said Vicky.

When their mother had left the room, Vicky said to Little Thomas, "Do you think she was a witch?"

"Who?" asked Little Thomas.

"The lady on the beach."

This time Little Thomas heard her. "Vicky!" he cried, shaking his sister by the shoulder. "Wake up! She's after us!"

"What?" mumbled Vicky sleepily. "Who? What's the matter?" And she tried to snuggle down and go back to sleep again.

"Vicky! Wake up! The witch is after us!"

Vicky sat up very suddenly, the sleep all gone from her head. "How do you know?" she demanded.

"I heard her singing," said Little Thomas. "I heard her ordering them to bring us out in our nighties." And he added in a trembling voice, "I haven't got my nightie on. Only my shirt."

"Well," said Vicky, "what we've got to do is hide from her."

"It's no use," said Little Thomas. "She knows we're

GEORGE GIBBS AND GUERNSEY MOORE

"Yes," said Little Thomas. "On account of the marzipan."

"Well," said Vicky, "we must be very careful."

They decided not to tell anybody, but they thought it would be all right to ask questions. That night at supper, with her mouth full of peanut butter, Vicky asked her father, "Did you ever see a witch?"

Michael Doyle gave his wife a twinkling, shining look. "I suppose," he said, "you don't mean your mother?"

"No," said Vicky.

"In that case," said her father, "I have nothing further to say."

Even Little Thomas could see that his father wasn't much help to them. And that night when the children were in bed the sea witch came to the house again, clutching the pail and the shovel and sang a song and wove a spell.

> *Pompano and grampus,*
> *Sea horse (Hippocampus),*
> *Barracuda, sea trout,*
> *Bring Tom and Vicky out.*

And she added as an afterthought:

> *Sea mice (Aphrodites)——*
> *In their nighties!*

here." And he added halfheartedly, "We could tell mother."

"She'd only say, 'Go back to sleep,'" said Vicky. "What we've got to do is to get out of here." She thought for a moment. "We'll go somewhere up the hill," she said, "where she won't find us."

"There's snakes on the hill in summer," said Little Thomas. "Public snakes."

"That's right," said Vicky. "I forgot. Well then," she said after a while, "we'll go way down on the beach somewhere, and she'll have to look for us so long she'll get tired. Put your space suit on; and I'll take my hope chest in case we need it."

The two children silently put on their warm wrappers, and Little Thomas put on his space suit over it because he was shivering; and Vicky took her hope chest, which already had 47¢ in it; and they tiptoed out of the room, making sure that the door didn't squeak behind them. They shuffled in the dark down the hall to the French windows, which opened onto the porch, and peeked out. "You go first," said Vicky.

"You go," said Little Thomas. "You're the oldest."

"But you're a boy," said Vicky.

"Well," said Little Thomas, "you're a bold girl and unafraid of mice."

So Vicky slipped out-of-doors into the gray, misty

night, followed by Little Thomas. Right away they began to run as hard as they could, which was a great mistake, because the minute they started to run the piggy bank began to jingle, and the witch heard them and was up and after them like a shot; whereas if they had gone very quietly she might never have known they were there.

They ran faster than they had ever run before in their lives, taking great leaps and hops, while their throats grew dry with fear and their breath came in gasps and their legs hurt. They fled like shadows through the dark, and the cold, wet, sticky fingers of the fog brushed their faces and clutched at them and let them go; and all the time the witch followed them like

*"Now it was summer and they went every day to the beach." A 1907* Post *cover by J. C. Leyendecker shows children enjoying the one playground of which they never tire. It is supplied with toys—shells, stones, seaweed—and with raw materials for the creative artist. Thanks to winds and tide, the beach is always changing, always new.*

a black wind, like the night itself, sniffing the air for their scent.

"Vicky," she cried, and her voice was like the edge of a breaking wave. "Little Thomas! Wait!"

"Oh, never!" sobbed Vicky, feeling the strength ooze out of her; and collapsed at last behind a pile of seaweed that made a deep black shadow all around her. A moment later Little Thomas sank to the ground beside her; and the two children crouched there together, shivering, holding their breath, listening like hunted rabbits to the sounds of the sea witch, rustling and snuffling in the sand.

Clutched to Vicky's soft little stomach, the hope chest made no noise; and the sea witch, momentarily baffled, stopped and peered through the darkness with her sad, nearsighted eyes, listening for the sound of heartbeats, her thin, beautiful nostrils flaring this way and that to catch the little-boy-and-girl smell, the bread-and-butter fragrance of children, among the iodine odors of the kelp.

When at last she realized that she had lost them, she sat down in the sand and began to weep.

Back of their dark shadowy pile of seaweed Little Thomas and his sister looked at each other in consternation. "She's crying," said Little Thomas. "She is sad."

"It isn't like what I expected," said Vicky.

"Do you think," asked Little Thomas, "that maybe we ought to go out and pat her on the head?"

"I don't know," said Vicky. "I never heard a witch cry before." And she added uncertainly, "Maybe she's lonesome."

"Maybe she only wanted to play with us or something," said Little Thomas.

"Why don't you go and ask her," said Vicky, clutching her hope chest firmly to her.

"I would," said Little Thomas doubtfully, "only— maybe she's crying because she's hungry."

"Hush," said Vicky; "she'll hear you."

Nevertheless, when the sea witch's sobbing had died down after a while to a mere foamy sniffle, the two children crept out of their hiding place, and with Vicky in the lead went slowly and with some misgivings toward where the sea witch lay like a shadow on the sand. "Don't cry," said Vicky in a small, scared voice; and Little Thomas said, "There, there," and gave her a timid pat on the head.

The sea witch started up in surprise. "Why," she cried, "how nice of you! I thought I had lost you, and I did so want to take you home with me."

"To eat?" asked Little Thomas, backing away and dropping his space helmet in the sand, so that he had to bend down to look for it. But the sea witch gave a

*Harvey T. Dunn, best known for Western prairie scenes, painted this 1928 shorescape.*

silvery laugh that sounded the way a school of minnows looks when it flashes by this way and that in the clear water. "Whatever gave you that idea?" she cried. "I only want to play with you."

"Oh," said Little Thomas, "in *that* case——"

"We'd like that very much," said Vicky politely.

The sea witch jumped to her feet and at once began calling in her spells from up and down the beach. "Pompano," she called. "Amber jack! Come back! Sea bass, Sea rover—give over! And all you currents, tides, and courses—the lost are found! Trumpet fish, sound! Hitch up my 12 sea horses! . . .

"We're going to have so much fun," she told the children. "Wait till you see the Grand Banks, and Fujiyama. Wait till you see Capri! And think of all the treasures: pearls and corals, grottoes and caves, the banquet halls of lobsters—necklaces of amethyst, minuets of angel fish——"

"Haven't you got any pirate ships?" asked Little Thomas.

"Dozens of them," said the sea witch happily, "all sunk in fathoms five and full of skeletons."

She put her arms around the children and led them gently down to the water. It was a curiously light feeling, they thought, almost as though they were being held up by water wings. Little Thomas kept thinking of the skeletons he was going to see, maybe with their heads chopped off or an arm or a leg missing; and Vicky felt a little afraid, as though what she was doing was very dangerous, and if she took a wrong step, who could tell—she might never come back.

"And so," said the sea witch under her breath to a barracuda that was swimming past, "she won't if I have anything to do with it!"

Not that she was really wicked—as she explained to Little Thomas later on, somewhere off Tierra del Fuego: she never ate meat, only vegetables, and fish on Fridays. The thing was, she was lonely, and tired of swimming about with only anchovies for company.

"If I can coax her into letting me have the hope chest," she thought; "if I can tempt her to spend her red real copper pennies for dreams, she'll never get away from me—never! I shall have her forever!"

She felt happy because she didn't think that any little girl would be able to resist the marvelous treasures she meant to show her.

Drawn by 12 magnificent sea horses, shaking the foam from their shoulders, and preceded by a band of trumpet fish scattering notes like drops of water, the sea witch and her two little companions swept through the clear, luminous sea, up and down the great green

*"Dressed like some one's nurse . . . with sad face and sea-colored eyes," Robert Nathan must have envisioned a sea witch resembling this lady who appeared on the Post with a copy of the Post in 1905. There is no record of the artist's name, and no hint as to the reason for her enigmatic expression.*

currents which ran like roads across the ocean floor. Past lost galleons they galloped, across mountains of coral glowing like sunsets, over the meadows of the sea, down into caves as blue as moonlight, past schools of sheepshead, croakers, minnows, mackerel, bass, zebra fish, goldfish—fish of every size, color, and shape; past squid and octopuses waving their weedlike arms, whales going by like battleships, tiny shrimp bobbing about in country dances. And every once in a while the sea witch would point to a great heap of pearls or a big lump of amethyst, or to piles and piles of golden doubloons, and ask hopefully, "Is this what you want? Will you buy it?" And every time, with a little gasp, Vicky would say, "No, thank you," and clutch her hope chest tighter.

They galloped up under the North Pole, and Vicky had a snowflake on her cheek, but when they got as far south as Oregon it melted. And in the coral seas there were a million golden stars reflected in the water, but when she reached for them they rippled away into nothing. "Will you buy? Will you buy?" cried the sea witch, but Vicky still said, "No."

She saw mermaids with little moons in their hair; they looked rare and curious, but they looked lonely too, without any fathers and mothers. "Stay here with us," they cried and held out their arms to her; but Vicky only said, "Thank you, but I don't think I want to."

She saw many things that were curious and rare—secret treasures that nobody knew about. They looked like her dreams—except that there was something the matter with them. They should have made her feel happy and beautiful, but they didn't; on the contrary, they made her feel sad and they gave her a lost, lone-

some feeling. Was it because she was really seeing them at last? She didn't know.

All she knew was that there wasn't anything she wanted to give up her hope chest for. And the strange part of it was that the more she saw of these wonderful things that didn't belong to her, the more she longed for the little, unwonderful things of her own: her father and mother around the breakfast table, her own cup of milk, the warm, cozy supper of bread and butter and rice pudding and Brussels sprouts, and her mother's good-night kiss.

"I do think," she said to herself in surprise, as they were rounding the Cape of Good Hope, "I do think that what I really want is just to be me—without any difference!"

When the sea witch saw that Vicky wouldn't part with her hope chest for any of the things she'd shown her, she grew very sad and silent and a little older, and drove them home by way of Catalina, Santa Monica, and Malibu. "Good-bye, Vicky," she said gently. "I thought I could get you to exchange the things you really need for things that are no use to you, but you were too wise for me. I don't hold it against you, because that's the way you are. You will grow up to be a lovely young woman, and marry and have little children of your own; and maybe someday I'll come back again when they're as old as you are now and see if they are all as wise as you."

She leaned down to Vicky and touched her hair. "I should like to give you a kiss," she said. "Just one, if you don't mind. May I?"

"Of course," said Vicky politely, holding up her face. The sea witch stooped to kiss it and dropped a single tear on Vicky's cheek.

As for Little Thomas, the sea witch shook him

DRAWN BY
SARAH B. STILWELL WEBER

*In 1916 little girls were little girls, even on the beach. They wore dresses trimmed with embroidery, ruffled petticoats, hats, and hair ribbons.*

DRAWN BY MRS. K. R. WIREMAN

*In 1906 a young lady went down to the sea in white skirt and shirtwaist, necktie, and pompadour hairdo.*

heartily by the hand. After that she gave a little cry and went into the sea in a long, beautiful arc and swam out on the tide, with her hair floating out behind her like seaweed.

Vicky and Little Thomas went home to bed. The morning star was in the sky, but it was still far from dawn.

Next morning, with the sun shining so bright, and a mockingbird singing outside the window, and the breakfast smell of coffee for the professor and cocoa for the children and bacon for everybody in the air, it

was hard to believe that it had all happened. Except that Little Thomas' hand was stained with a greenish color, like kelp, for several days, and on Vicky's cheek there was a little pattern like a snowflake. "You probably slept on it," said Mrs. Doyle, "and got a crease."

But that didn't explain why, ever afterward, whenever Vicky kissed anyone, she was told it was like being kissed by a breath from the sea.

Or why, when the hope chest was opened at last to buy a silver spoon and two linen pillowcases for Vicky's wedding, a little piece of dried seaweed fell out.

# The Spell of the Shell

The shells most commonly found on beaches are of three types. *Univalves* are single units usually—but not always—coiled like a snailshell. Most spiral to the right, or clockwise, but a few nonconformists curl in the opposite direction. *Bivalves* have two identical parts connected by a hinge—these include the familiar clamshells, oysters, and scallops. There are also *tooth shells* which are tubelike and tapering with an opening in each end. Some tooth shells curve slightly, like an elephant's tusk, while others bend into wiggly spirals.

Mollusks live in all seas, and shells wash up onto all the beaches of the world, but tropical species are the most varied and colorful.

At every moment of history, men have treasured some shells for their beauty, rarity, or usefulness. Shells have served as objects for personal adornment, as dippers and drinking vessels, material for making fishhooks, musical instruments, magic charms, and money.

Colorful inch-long cowries from the South Pacific became a form of currency recognized throughout Asia and much of Europe for centuries, and beads cut from clamshells formed the wampum belts that served American Indians as money and also as a substitute for written records.

Since about 1700 shell collecting has been a popular hobby and rich men have been willing to pay large sums for specimens that are both beautiful and rare. The founders of the Shell Oil Company were sons of a London merchant named Marcus Samuel who traded in rare shells. It was his fortune that bankrolled the sons' venture into oil, reason enough for the sons to choose a shell for their business name and their logo.

Long before it symbolized oil, the scallop shell had religious significance. This kind of shell was common on a beach near the tomb of St. James in Spain, and it became the symbol of the saint. Men who had made the pilgrimage to the tomb wore scallop shells on their coats, and later the scallop shell became the symbol of any pilgrimage to a religious shrine.

Because of its graceful symmetry, the scallop shell was a favorite motif of architects and artists, and it forms the boat from which a nude goddess rises in Botticelli's *Birth of Venus*.

If the scallop is the most artistic of shells, the conch (pronounced "conk") is the most musical. The conch is a large spiral univalve used as a trumpet in many parts of the world, because many different primitive peoples discovered that by boring a small hole in one end of a conch and then blowing into it, they could produce a loud, far-carrying sound. The conch is also the shell that "sings"—hold it to your ear and you will hear what resembles the murmuring of far-off surf. (Actually, the sound you hear is the blood coursing through blood vessels in your own ear acoustically amplified by the shell's curved chamber. Basically, the conch "sings" for the same reason it makes a good trumpet.)

Shell collecting is today one of the most popular of all hobbies, a favorite activity of children, elderly people, and lots of others in between. You can acquire shells by buying them, or by trading with other collectors, but by far the most pleasant way is to hunt them for yourself, strolling barefoot at the edge of a sunny sea.

*Fashions change, but not a child's delight in sea, sand, and shells. A 1909 painting by Sarah S. Stilwell Weber.*

*Always new, a child's wonder at the murmuring song of a shell. A 1927* Post *cover painting by Ellen Pyle.*

# Yes, My Daring Daughter

*Until well after World War I, ladies went down to the sea encumbered by ruffles and flounces. Bathing beauties who took part in the first Miss America contest in 1921 wore long black stockings, and as late as 1937 Atlantic City banned men without tops. It all seems very quaint to a generation that has survived miniskirt, bikini, and Rudi Gernreich's 1965 introduction of a topless suit for women, gone skinny-dipping at Woodstock and hot-tub soaking in California, but this 1949 essay indicates that the beach has ever been a beachhead in the battle for one kind of freedom.*

COLES PHILLIPS

O f all the trends discernible in the history of America, including even those endless changes which have come over our fashions in wearing apparel since the wonderful days of the late Ulysses S. Grant, the evolution of women's bathing

suits is unique in this: instead of following the erratic course common to other trends, veering aimlessly or slipping back or repeating itself, the trend in bathing suits has for 70 consecutive years marched in the same direction and toward a single fixed objective.

The credit for this remarkable consistency belongs to the American girl. The feat, in fact, could not have been accomplished by anyone else; for, in bringing about the evolution of the bathing suit, she displayed the steadfastness of purpose that can always be expected of her when she sets out to get her own way about something.

It was not easy in this case; she encountered plenty of opposition while she was gradually whittling her

*Beach styles from the generous years.
On this page, a demure and well-covered
belle by Harrison Fisher (1908).
Opposite: a daringly bare-kneed
beauty by Coles Phillips (1920) and an
over-endowed bather with water-wings
by J. C. Leyendecker (1922).*

original beach
attirc to its prcscnt thrifty
proportions.

She braved paternal wrath and
sand fleas; she risked sunburn and police
action; she persisted despite editorial mum-
blings and scoldings from the pulpit. And her crusading
spirit, far from dimming, flamed anew each summer
when the time came to make her appearance on the
beach in the newest version of the bathing suit. The
public attention it brought down on her, the murmurs
and gasps, the concerted stare of bold male eyes—all
these she endured, and endured unflinchingly, gladly,
and as often as possible.

Her reward can be seen today on beaches and lake
shores everywhere. The untrammeled freedom now
being enjoyed by our bathing girls—and the spectators—is something Miss America won for herself. Having completely fulfilled her determination to throw off
the shackles of the past, she can now rest content. She
must, in fact. There is nothing more to throw.

*Bathing-suit ads from 1930 and (opposite page) a 1933* Post *cover by John LaGatta. The ruffles were gone, as were the stockings. The bathing suit had become a sleek, bright-colored garment that fitted like a second skin. Partly responsible for the change was a Portland, Oregon, sweater manufacturer named Carl Jantzen. He belonged to a rowing club, and in Oregon rowers are nearly always wet and cold. In 1913 club members talked Jantzen into making them suits from the wool ribbing used for sweater cuffs. Snug yet stretchy, warm even when wet, the new kind of suit was a hit with swimmers as well as rowers. By the middle '20s it was seen on all beaches, along with the new rubber beach balls and the rubber bathing caps that were supposed to keep a lady's hair dry, though they never did.*

# "Must I Go Down to the Beach Again?"

## BY JOHN SKOW

A beach is not a fit place to be. This is well understood by the entire animal kingdom, excepting only the sandpiper, who is nitwitted; the crocodile, who is squamous; the sea lion, who thinks the sandpiper knows something; and man. In this respect, as in others, man has not ripened into wisdom. Ages ago, when man's ancestor first poked his head from the tidal wash and noticed evolution's eon sign, he did not waste his slime on the beach. He slithered across it at top speed (thinking the sign belonged to a bar and grill), noticing only that the sand scraped his belly and that the moss that came afterward helped a lot.

*Fun on the beach. On this page, detail from a 1952* Post *cover by George Hughes. Opposite page: a 1960 cover by James Williamson.*

In the last few decades of the present eon, however, man has grown perversely bored with the green-growing golf course, the black-flowering asphalt, and the clear-bubbling cocktail lounge, and he has strayed wistfully back toward the sea. There, where the solid leaves off and the liquid begins, he has found and cherished an intermediate state of matter. It is a damp mulch of mustardy hot-dog wrappers, fat ladies, displeased infants, former fish, ex-seaweed, volleyball players, lost socks, midget radios, walruses, beer cans, pieces of sodden wood that look even uglier when they are turned into lamps, big pink men with little white legs, uncomfortable small stones, other people's elderly lunch in moist brown bags, insolent sea gulls, and bugs. Not to mention shrieks shouts squeaks roars and baseball scores, five-year-old girls in two-piece suits, small boys glistening with cherry soda, young mothers oiling themselves and planning to take a course in something, dismayed fathers, impatient businessmen, brain-fried lifeguards, scornful teenagers, addled dogs, and me—talked into it all again, despite a vivid memory that this was the way it was last time.

(The author writhes in distress. He thinks he is at the beach, with the deadly August sun beating down. Actually he has fallen asleep on the living-room sofa, as he always does if he drinks a beer with lunch, and it is merely a ceiling light fixture that is causing his eyes to squinch. It is not August but March. However—there is reason for the author's daymare. There is a Surf-'n'-Sun Sale at the local female chandlery, and his wife has gone there with car and charge-plate to buy a bikini.)

The delirium enters a new phase. The author's wife and children are propelling him toward the family station wagon. He struggles. "Since you asked," he says to his three-year-old, "my objection is that you can't *do* anything on a beach. You can't play pinochle comfortably; the sand makes the cards gritty. The same with hand-holding and other gestures of emotion. You can't read; the sun is too bright and children drip on your book. You can't swim because you saw a baby shark on the sand. You can't sleep for a dozen reasons. Sand castles are silly. Volleyball is for morons, and anyway, if you're overweight you jiggle. To sum up, you drive 90 miles, park,

walk, undress, dress, walk, put down the towel, smear on the lotion, and there you are: 90 miles from sanity, covered with linseed oil, lying on a highly efficient abrasive, and what is there to do?''

The dream bursts. The author's wife, wearing snowy boots, fake-fur winter coat, and ski hat, is standing by the living-room sofa, saying something that ends with ''. . . thought you were going to watch the kids the baby got the chain saw.''

''Sorry.'' Slowly the world comes into focus.

''Well, anyway, let me show you.'' His wife leaves the room with her packages and comes back dressed sparsely in green nylon. The author is numbed with horror. It is a rather nice bikini, and it is a rather nice wife. But the combination means that August, gritty and peeling, and glistening with oil and cherry soda, is going to come again. The author weaves to the icebox for another beer, and then goes outside to stand in a snowbank.

# Don't Envy the Lifeguard

## BY EMMETT MURPHY

I don't know who started the story, but I do know that it is a generally accepted belief that a lifeguard is a lucky fellow whose daily routine combines the perquisites and pleasures of a sultan and a Hollywood star. According to this pipe dream, a lifeguard is a bronzed Apollo who suns himself daily, absorbing quantities of vitamin D, to the accompanying admiration of dozens of adoring females, all resembling Lana Turner.

This routine is occasionally broken up, according to legend, by heroic rescues of blond beauties who have willfully swum into the riptide on a dare. When these limp but lithesome bodies are towed to shore by our hero, there is always a gentleman in a silk hat and frock coat who steps forward, introduces himself as the father, a man of millions, and then gets down to brass tacks by saying, "That's my daughter, young man. There's a place in my business for you. Also my daughter's hand in marriage, if you choose to accept."

I hate to prick this pleasant fantasy. But, with the authority of a lifeguard who has worked both the Atlantic and the Pacific, I must say that this version of a lifeguard's life resembles actuality the same way that Mickey Rooney resembles Gregory Peck. . . .

The great majority of lifeguards have tedious jobs. Not only do they sit in the broiling sun all day, squinting at the water, but they must also observe the foolish and sometimes criminally negligent behavior of their fellows on the loose. They also function as information centers, custodians of handbags, nursemaids, backdrops for group photographs, and, betimes, collectors of rags, bottles, and watermelon rinds. In between, they pull people out of the water.

To be sure, there may be beaches where the guards live the life of Riley, but these are in the minority. When you see a lifeguard lolling on the beach, taking his ease before a miniature harem, hang your clothes on a hickory limb, but don't go near the water.

Lifeguards have to practice their skills, and sometimes the customers mistake our mock rescues for the real thing. Last summer we had just pulled one guard in from the water and were going through the motions of reviving him when a small but imperious gentleman stepped forward. Obviously he knew all there was to know about artificial respiration. He took the proceedings very seriously and barked an occasional command.

Nobody paid much attention to him until, unable to contain himself any longer, he shoved the straddling lifeguard to one side. "Here's the way it should be done," he bellowed, plumping himself down on the recumbent figure.

The pseudovictim howled in anguish and sat up.

"See?" said the intruder. "I get quick results!"

Sometimes we don't have the nerve to tell these would-be heroes that it's all just a practice session. More than one middle-aged man has gone home and told a glowing story to his wife about how he, practically single-handed, saved a life.

We let him think so. Why spoil his fun?

We count that day lost when there aren't a half dozen requests to find a lost ring. One woman that I pulled in out of fairly shallow water started to bleat hysterically when I got her up on the beach. At first I thought it was hysteria because of near drowning. But she got her breath and said, "Go back! You've got to go back and get it! I lost my good-luck ring in the water!" The one thing that people almost never say when we haul them out of the water is "Thank you."

Contrary to popular opinion, a guard usually sees rather than hears trouble. When you have 50,000 people sprawled on a beach, the cacophony would drown out any plaintive call for help. Anyway, most people in trouble in the water are so busy gasping for air that they can't let out even a peep. That's why your guard, if he's on the job, sits high on his perch, remote from all comers, including blondes who invite him down to have his picture taken. . . .

A lifeguard gets to know the danger symptoms. He's got to know whether that portly gent is doing a dead man's float voluntarily or whether he's in trouble. He's got to keep his eye out for little girls in inner tubes. Meanwhile he's busy answering questions. Although he's isolated from all humanity, he's supposed to know whether the Dodgers are ahead or not; what the most direct route to Springfield is; and where there's a good place to eat.

When he isn't busy answering questions and scanning the water for trouble, likely as not he's being regarded with disdain by a group of girls who want to borrow his blanket and who would like to have him sit in on the picture. But the number of doting females is far fewer than the number of buxom mothers who shout at you, wanting to know if you have seen a small boy in yellow trunks. Because nine times out of ten you haven't seen a small boy in yellow trunks, the mother gets hysterical. So then you peer a little harder, and your heart pounds faster as

you scan the water. Almost invariably at that point the boy in the yellow trunks appears on the scene. He'd just gone back to the car for his pail. . . .

*J. C. Leyendecker painted this lifeguard basking in sunshine and admiration.*
*(1932)*

# All About Sailboats

## BY JAMES THURBER

*On these two pages, sailboats painted by Anton Otto Fischer.*

People who visit you in Bermuda are likely to notice, even before they notice the flowers of the island, the scores of sailing craft which fleck the harbors and the ocean round about. Furthermore, they are likely to ask you about the ships before they ask you about the flowers and this, at least in my own case, is unfortunate, because although I know practically nothing about flowers I know ten times as much about flowers as I know about ships. Or at any rate I did before I began to study up on the subject. Now I feel that I am pretty well qualified to hold my own in any average discussion of rigging.

I began to brush up on the mysteries of sailing a boat after an unfortunate evening when a lady who sat next to me at dinner turned to me and said, "Do you reef in your gaff-topsails when you are close-hauled or do you let go the mizzen-top-bowlines and crossjack-braces?" She took me for a sailor and not a landlubber and I hadn't the slightest idea what she was talking about.

One reason for this was that none of the principal words (except "reef") used in the sentence I have quoted is pronounced the way it is spelled: "gaff-top-sails" is pronounced "gassles," "close-hauled" is pronounced "cold," "mizzen-top-bowlines" is pronounced "mittens," and "crossjack-braces" is pronounced "crabapples" or something that sounds a whole lot like that. Thus what the lady really said to me was, "Do you reef in your gassles when you are cold or do you let go the mittens and crabapples?" Many a visitor who is asked such a question takes the first ship back home, and it is for these embarrassed gentlemen that I am going to explain briefly the history and terminology of sailing.

In the first place, there is no doubt but that the rigging of the modern sailing ship has become complicated beyond all necessity. If you want proof of this you have only to look up the word "rigging" in the *Encyclopedia Britannica*. You will find a drawing of a full-rigged modern ship and under it an explanation of its various spars, masts, sails, etc. There are 45 different major parts, beginning with "bowsprit" and going on up to "davit topping lifts." Included in between are, among others, these items: the fore-topmast staysail halyards (pron. "fazzles"), the topgallant mast-yard-and-lift (pron. "toft"), the mizzen-topgallant-braces (pron. "mazes"), and the fore-topmast backstays and topsail tye (pron. "frassantossle"). The tendency of the average landlubber who studies this diagram for five minutes is to turn to "Sanskrit" in the encyclopedia and study up on that instead, but only a coward would do that. It is possible to get something out of the article on rigging if you keep at it long enough.

Let us creep up on the formidable modern sailing ship in our stocking feet, beginning with one of the simplest of all known sailing craft, the Norse Herring Boat. Now when the Norse built their sailing boats they had only one idea in mind: to catch herring. They were pretty busy men, always a trifle chilly, and they had neither the time nor the inclination to sit around on the cold decks of their ships trying to figure out all the different kinds of ropes, spars, and sails that might be hung on their masts. Each ship had, as a matter of fact, only one mast. Near the top of it was a crosspiece of wood and on that was hung one simple square sail, no more complicated than the awning of a cigar store. A rope was attached to each end of the crosspiece and the other ends of these ropes were held by the helmsman. By manipulating the ropes he could make the ship go ahead, turn right, or turn left. It was practically impossible to make it turn around, to be sure, and that is the reason the Norsemen went straight on and discovered America, thus proving that it isn't really necessary to turn around.

As the years went on and the younger generations of Norsemen became, like all younger generations, less hardworking and more restless than their forebears, they began to think less about catching herring and more about monkeying with the sails of their ships. One of these restless young Norsemen one day lengthened the mast of his ship, put up another crosspiece about six feet above the first one, and hung another but smaller sail on this new crosspiece, or spar (pronounced, strange as it may seem, "spar"). Thus was the main topsail born.

After that, innovations in sails followed so fast that the herring boat became a veritable shambles of canvas. A Norseman named Leif the Sailmaker added a second mast to his ship, just in front of the first one, and thus the foremast came into being and with it the fore mainsail and the fore-topsail. A Turk named Skvar added a third mast and called it the mizzen. Not to be outdone, a Muscovite named Amir put up a third spar on each of his masts; Skvar put up a fourth; Amir replied with a fifth; Skvar came back with a sixth, and so it went, resulting in the topgallant foresail, the top-topgallant mizzen sail, the top-top-topgallant main topsail, and the tip-top-topgallant-gallant mainsail (pron. "twee twee twee twa twa").

Practically nobody today sails a full-rigged seven-masted ship so that it would not be especially helpful to describe in detail all the thousands of different gaffs, sprits, queeps, weems, lugs, miggets, loords (spelled "leewards"), gessels, grommets, etc., on such a ship. I shall therefore devote what space I have left to a discussion of how to come back alive from a pleasant sail in the ordinary 20- or 30-foot sailing craft such as

*James Thurber described the racing sailboat as a "so-called pleasure craft . . . given to riding on its side."*

you are likely to be "taken for a ride" in down here in Bermuda. This type of so-called pleasure ship is not only given to riding on its side, due to coming about without the helmsman's volition (spelled "jibe" and pronounced "look out, here we go again!"), but it is made extremely perilous by what is known as the flying jib, or boom.

The boom is worse than the gaff for some people can stand the gaff (hence the common expression "he can stand the gaff") but nobody can stand the boom when it aims one at him from the floor. With the disappearance of the Norse herring fisherman and the advent of the modern pleasure-craft sailor, the boom became longer and heavier and faster. Helmsmen will tell you that they keep swinging the boom across the deck of the ship in order to take advantage of the wind but after weeks of observation it is my opinion that they do it to take advantage of the passengers. The only way to avoid the boom and have any safety at all while sailing is to lie flat on your stomach in the bottom of the ship. This is very uncomfortable on account of the hard boards and because you can't see a thing, but it is the one sure way I know of to go sailing and come back on the boat and not be washed up in the surf. I recommend the posture highly, but not as highly as I recommend the bicycle. My sailing adventures in Bermuda have made me appreciate for the first time the essential wonder of the simple, boomless bicycle.

*Can this marriage be saved? Dick Sargent's 1959* Post *cover reflects both the joys and the discomforts of small-boat sailing.*

# My Life in the Navy

## BY NORMAN ROCKWELL

When the first draft call of World War I was sent out, I was declared exempt. I don't remember why; maybe, with all my wife's relatives, I had too many dependents. Still, I felt guilty, so when the authorities organized a harbor patrol in New Rochelle to guard the approaches to Fort Slocum, a big enlistment center, I joined up.

Headquarters of the harbor patrol was an old bug-infested yawl anchored in the middle of Pelham Bay. One night a week I would report to the yawl with my friend Clyde Forsythe, the cartoonist. Our captain would assign us to a rowboat loaded with rifles and pistols, and we'd row with muffled oarlocks about the bay, listening for the swish and clank of German submarines surfacing. All we ever intercepted was a rowboat carrying two women on their way to cheer up the boys at Fort Slocum.

In the daytime, of course, I stuck to my easel. The papers were full of war news, and every headline suggested an idea for a magazine cover. "French Populace Cheers Doughboys"—I did a magazine cover showing a little French girl inserting a poppy in an American soldier's buttonhole. "Sergeant Awarded Croix de Guerre, Bussed by French General"—I painted a startled doughboy being kissed on the cheek by a French general. Four other illustrators read the same news item and did covers on it. When four magazines came out in the same week with covers of a French general kissing a doughboy, everybody called up everybody else and threatened to sue.

I was pretty well satisfied with myself, knocking out covers and illustrations for the *Post, Country Gentleman, Leslie's, Life,* and *Judge,* enjoying my fan mail, and making quite a bit of money. Then, one day in June, 1917, I decided it was my duty to enlist. The doctors at Pelham Bay Naval Enlistment Headquarters rejected me because I was 17 pounds underweight for my height and age, so I caught a train to New York, to try again at an enlistment center at City Hall.

The yeoman who weighed me there had been a student at the Art Students League. "You've overdone the starving-artist bit," he said. "We'll have to talk to a doctor."

He led me into a dark little office and explained my

*Sailor and girl—detail from a 1960* Post *cover by ex-Navyman Norman Rockwell.*

problem to a doctor who was sitting with his feet up on a desk and smoking a cigar.

"How much under is he?" asked the doctor, looking thoughtfully at my nakedness.

"Seventeen pounds," said the yeoman.

"Won't do," said the doctor. "We can waive 10 pounds, but not 17."

The yeoman glanced furtively around.

"How about the treatment?" he whispered.

"He don't look big enough," said the doctor.

"I want to get in," I said, shivering as chill drafts ran up and down my bare legs. "What's the treatment?"

"Bananas, doughnuts, and water," said the doctor.

"You eat seven pounds' worth, we waive the other ten pounds, and you're in." He pulled open a file drawer. It was filled with bananas and doughnuts. I eased onto an icy chair, my teeth chattering. The yeoman drew a pitcher of water at the washbasin in the corner. The doctor heaped bananas and doughnuts around it. "Go to it," he said.

I began to eat and drink. After a while I staggered to the scales—five pounds to go. So I ate some more and drank some more. The doctor's cigar went out. The yeoman watched me intently.

"I'm going to burst," I said. "I'd better quit."

But the doctor and the yeoman had now adopted my enlistment as a personal cause; it wasn't just one sailor more or less, it was their battle against the Kaiser and all his forces of darkness.

"Come on," said the doctor, peeling a banana, "four more doughnuts, and bananas, and more water."

I stuffed. And stuffed. And stuffed. The yeoman weighed me again. "We've won!" he shouted. I could hardly walk; the seven pounds of doughnuts, bananas, and water sloshing about in my stomach threw me off balance. But I managed to struggle into my clothes and totter home.

A few days later I was ordered to report to the Brooklyn Navy Yard, where I would embark for the base at Queenstown, Ireland. We sailed that night, but a warning that German submarines were lurking off the coast brought a change of course. The next morning we docked at Charleston, South Carolina. Flu was raging through the camp; men were dying every day. Being shorthanded, the authorities assigned new arrivals to guard duty and burial squads. I got a piece of both.

Guard duty was cold, damp, and frightening, but uneventful. I just stood in a mud puddle for four hours, scared of snakes, Germans, and my fellow guards, who would shoot at anything which made a noise. At dusk 12 of us were issued guns and marched off to the cemetery, behind a wagon laden with rough pine coffins. As each one was lowered into a grave, the officer said, "Readyaimfire," and we fired—bangety, bang, bang, bang . . . bang. That last bang was from me; I hardly knew the butt of a rifle from the barrel.

The next day I was assigned to the camp newspaper, *Afloat and Ashore*, to draw cartoons and make layouts two days a week. The rest of the time I could do my own work, as long as it was in some way related to the Navy. I painted a *Post* cover of one sailor showing another a picture of his girl, and a cover for the humor magazine *Life* of a group of smiling soldiers, sailors, and marines. I drew countless portraits of officers and enlisted men. Doing portraits of officers made my life less complicated. If I wanted a pass to town, I'd just ask one of my sitters. He could hardly refuse; I might have elongated his nose or weakened his chin.

A few months later all the men in special services were alarmed to hear that a new commander had been appointed to the Charleston Naval Base. A sailor named O'Toole was discussing the situation with me one afternoon when the studio door was flung open, a voice yelled "ten-SHUN!", and in walked the new base commander, a big, handsome, beefy-looking fellow in dress uniform. His smartly dressed wife accompanied him.

"Carry on, men, carry on," he said. I went back to work on a portrait, and O'Toole fussed with a pile of old canvases in the corner. The new commander looked at the portrait on my easel, asked about my work, and left. O'Toole said that the new commander could be "got around." But the wife worried him.

The next day I was transferred to the commander's personal staff and went to live on the U.S.S. *Hartford*, which had been Admiral Farragut's flagship during the Civil War. Now it was moored in Charleston harbor as the official headquarters and residence of the commander of the Charleston Naval Base.

The *Hartford* had been refurbished since its fighting days in Mobile Bay. I shared a plush stateroom with a tenor and O'Toole, whom I had placed as chauffeur on the base-commander's staff by drawing a portrait of the ensign in charge of transportation. When the commander entertained visiting dignitaries, the tenor sang and I displayed my work before the assembled guests.

I soon learned that one of my jobs on the *Hartford* was to paint portraits of Capt. Mark St. Clair Ellis and his wife, who was very wealthy. I did two portraits of Captain Ellis, one in uniform and one in civilian clothes. All his ribbons had to be just so. He wanted his eyes to have just the right sparkle—lively, but dignified and stern.

I was just finishing the second portrait when the false armistice burst upon us. Everyone knew the real thing wasn't far off, and most of us applied for a discharge. To prevent a stampede, the Navy ruled that no honorable discharges were to be granted. All leaves were canceled too.

Well, I wanted to get out real bad. So I told Captain Ellis that the only place in the country where truly beautiful frames could be bought was Knoedler's in New York.

"I can pick out just the right ones," I said, "big, ornate, gold-leafed. They'll make the portraits look marvelous."

*Rockwell's neighbor and fellow illustrator Mead Schaeffer*
*posed as the tattoo artist whose client has had a*
*girl in every port. (1944)*

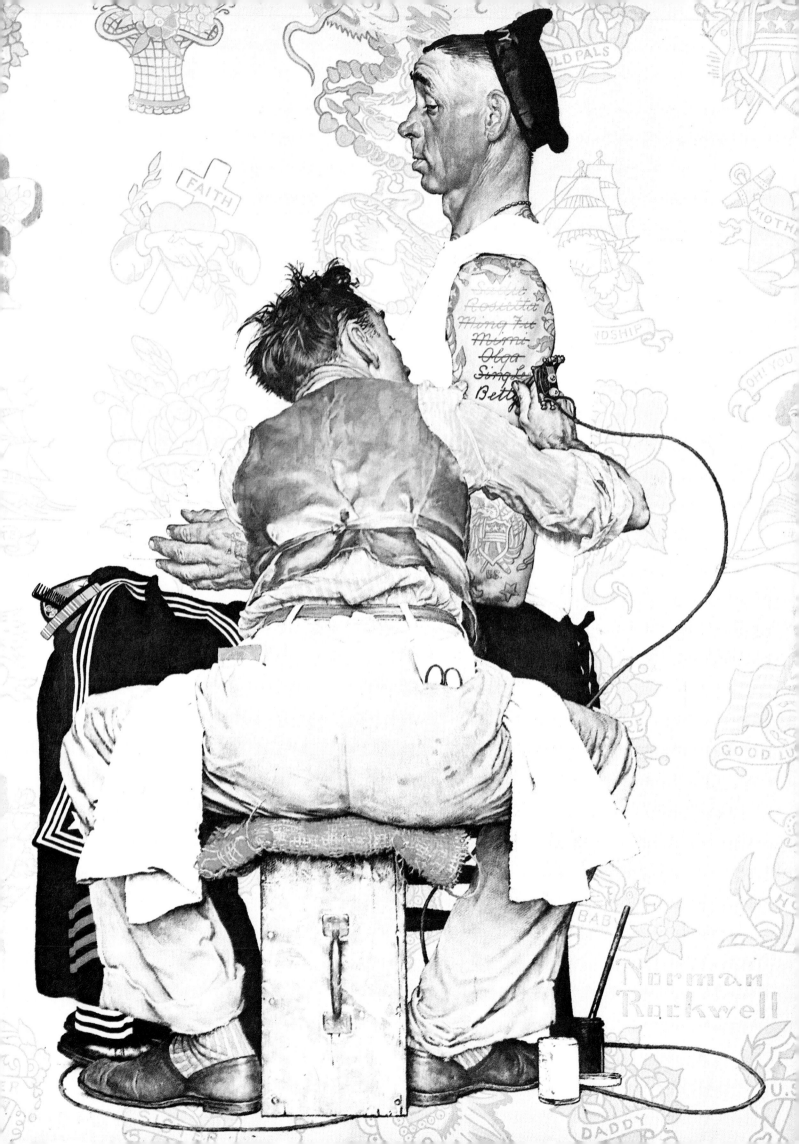

*J. C. Leyendecker painted this World War I recruiting poster in 1917, the same year his younger colleague Norman Rockwell joined the Navy.*

The aide reported that under the temporary order prohibiting honorable discharges, there were only two ways to get me out of the Navy at once: a dishonorable discharge, or an "inaptitude" discharge.

"Give him that inaptitude thing," said Mrs. Ellis.

"Good heavens!" said Captain Ellis. "He can't go through life with an inaptitude discharge! What'll his friends say—that he's a moron?"

"Don't be silly, Mark," said Mrs. Ellis, and she worked at him until he consented to sign me out.

On November 12, 1918, one day after the real armistice, I was discharged as unable to adapt myself to the duties of a "Landsman for Quartermaster" in the United States Naval Air Reserve. My service record reads:

Discharged with Inaptitude Discharge. Rockwell is an artist and unaccustomed to hard manual labor. His patriotic impulse caused him to enlist in a rating for which he has no aptitude.

Moreover, he is unsuited to Naval routine and hard work.

And below this is the terse comment:

I concur in the above statement.

(signed) Norman Rockwell

The Great
Adventures

Gordon Grant

# The Greatest Voyage Ever Made

## BY SAMUEL ELIOT MORISON

*The distinguished historian who wrote this account of Columbus' voyage for the* Post *in 1959 is best known as author of* Christopher Columbus, Mariner *and the two-volume* The European Discovery of America.

Christopher Columbus did more to chart the course of history than any other individual since the Emperor Augustus. He was the sign and symbol of a new age of hope and glory; he closed the book of the Middle Ages and wrote the first page of the modern era. The Americans are legatees of his faith and wisdom. The voyage of discovery that took him to "The Indies" and home was no blind chance, but his own creation, long studied, carefully planned, carried through by virtue of his courage, sea knowledge, and indomitable will. No later voyage could ever have such spectacular results, and Columbus' fame would have been secure had he retired from the sea in 1493.

Yet there is a strange paradox in his career. He never accomplished what he was trying to do; he never did find a new, short sea route from Europe to Eastern Asia. What he achieved was accidental, although of a magnitude that he never even imagined. On his third voyage, in 1498, after he had touched the American continent at Venezuela and observed the vast volume of fresh water flowing from the Orinoco, he did indeed write, "This is an Other World." But he died believing that this New or Other World of his discovery lay in about the same relations to the Asiatic continent that Indonesia actually does to Malaya. For him, Japan and China were always just around the next headland, and it remained for Magellan to find out how really remote they were.

At the age of 33, when Christopher Columbus dropped everything to promote his great idea, he was tall and well built, with high cheekbones and aquiline nose. His red hair had already turned white, but his complexion remained clear and ruddy. He had the air of authority proper to a master mariner, and the manners of a *hidalgo*, or gentleman. He was pleasant and affable in conversation unless provoked by ill-mannered stupidity, when he became irascible, and swore "By San Fernando!" or, "May God take you!" His tastes in eating, drinking, clothing, and amusements were moderate, even sober. Intensely religious, as befitted a man who believed that God had chosen him to implement a divine plan, Columbus observed the daily offices of the Church, fasted regularly, attended mass frequently, passed long hours in meditation, began and closed his letters with the sign of the cross or a little prayer. He was "as sure he would discover what he did discover," said his early biographer, Las Casas, "as if he held it in a chamber under lock and key."

Like most men possessed of a great idea, Columbus was a terrible bore to many people. He could never keep off the subject of what he could do if the king would only give him a fleet. In the hour of success he was too fond of saying "What a fool you were!" to people who had opposed or ridiculed him, and so made them eager to pull him down. He was overgreedy for gold, titles, and honors, a trait understandable in one who had known poverty in that age when the rich had everything and the poor nothing. The Spanish girl whom he took for a mistress after the death of his wife, and who bore him his son, Ferdinand, he never married. But there is no doubt that his faith was whole and sincere. The conviction that God had chosen him as an instrument for opening Asia to Christianity was more potent a motive than glory and personal enrichment.

Every educated person in Columbus' day accepted the sphericity of the earth; the round globe was the basis of geography as taught in schools and universities. The story that Columbus alone thought the world was round, and that people opposed his voyage because they believed in a flat earth and that ships would fall off the edge if they sailed too far is pure myth. People like the Russians, who lived on broad plains, may have believed the earth to be flat, but no sailor could have done so, after observing the sails of ships whose hulls were invisible below the horizon. Nor could dwellers on mountainous coasts, like those of Genoa, Spain, and Portugal, have believed in a flat earth, because they had only to climb a hill to see the horizon recede and islands appear that were invisible from sea level.

Columbus' trouble in getting people to support him was not the shape of the earth, but

Adventurers

*Norman Rockwell's 1928* Post *cover is a tribute to Columbus and the other master navigators who mapped the world we know.*

its size. By a series of miscalculations, making out the globe to be about one-fourth smaller and the length of Eurasia about 50 percent greater than they really are, he figured that a voyage of 2,400 nautical miles from the Canary Islands would take him to Japan, and a voyage of 3,550 miles to the coast of China. The actual airline distances are 10,600 and 11,766 miles, respectively! The eggheads of 1490 did not know that, but they did know that Columbus' calculations were very, very wrong. He expected to find Japan about where Florida actually is, and the coast of China at about the mouth of the Mississippi, in relation to Spain. That is why he had to appeal to the intuition of a great lady—Queen Isabella—before he could win support.

The queen, though she could not make up her mind for years, had an inkling from the first that Columbus "had something." Isabella, too, was a redhead and very beautiful. They were of exactly the same age—40. They reasoned much the same way, intuitively; and each was impressed by the other's dignity and sincerity. The experts, to be sure, insisted that his project was impractical, but the queen had seen a good deal of experts, and believed that most of them did not know what they were talking about. After all, nobody had sailed very far out into the ocean; Columbus' ideas as to its width might be better than those of the royal commissioners.

For five or six years, the queen kept Columbus dangling, as it were, with a tiny pension. It was in April, 1492, that he appeared before the sovereigns in the audience chamber of the Moorish palace at Granada, and was told that his proposals were accepted. By the end of May, 1492, everything was down in black and white. "Cristobal Colon," as Cristoforo Colombo had Hispanicized his name, was to be governor general over any islands or mainlands he might discover, with the titles of Viceroy of the Indies and Admiral of the Ocean Sea; and these titles would be hereditary. He should have 10 percent of all precious stones and metals mined or obtained by trade with the Orient. He was given a passport describing him as sailing with three caravels "toward the regions of India for certain reasons and purposes," together with letters of introduction conveying greetings from Ferdinand and Isabella, with blank spaces where he could insert the proper name and title of any potentate he might encounter.

The scene now shifts to Palos. This little town in Andalusia was chosen as the port of departure because three prominent shipowning families there—Pinzon, Nino, and Quintero—were "sold" on Columbus and could be counted on to recruit men. The fitting out of the three vessels cost only about $15,000 in gold. Most

of this was borrowed by the Crown from a fund that had been collected to support the police of Castile. The payroll, which amounted to about $1,750 a month, was assumed by the Crown.

At Barcelona there may still be seen a reasonably accurate replica of the flagship, the *Santa Maria*. She was 80 to 90 feet long, rigged with a short foremast carrying a lower course and topsail, a tall mainmast carrying a big lower course and small topsail, and a mizzenmast on the high poop, carrying a lateen sail.

The two other vessels were caravels, easy to handle and good at windward work. *Nina*, the smallest, became Columbus' favorite. Her burden was 60 tons, her length 65 to 70 feet. *Pinta*, fastest of the three, was slightly larger. Each caravel carried a square foresail, a square mainsail, and a lateen mizzen, but no topsails.

These vessels were well built, rigged and properly equipped for a long voyage. Columbus himself described them in his sea journal as "well suited for such an enterprise." His only complaint, and that against *Santa Maria*, was her slow speed compared with the two lively caravels. But the really surprising thing about these vessels to a modern sailor is their speed. On the outward passage in 1492, the fleet averaged eight knots for five days' running, and on one day of the homeward passage *Nina* and *Pinta* covered nearly 200 nautical miles, hitting 11 knots in the gusts. Racing yachts can better that today, but few if any commercial sailing vessels of their size 50 years ago could have surpassed their speed. How did they do it? Mainly by the pull of their big square sails. *Santa Maria*, for instance, had a main yard as long as the ship, and a mainmast that extended 90 feet above her keel. Such a press of sail made her pitch and roll abominably, but it certainly did drive her when the wind served.

Thanks to the researches of the late Alice Gould, we have an almost complete roster of the officers and men of the three vessels. *Nina* carried 22, *Pinta* 26 and *Santa Maria* 39. With few exceptions they were sailors of the Niebla, the region around Palos, recruited through the influence of the Pinzon, Nino, and Quintero families, several members of whom shipped as officers. Three of these lads of Palos had recently rescued from jail a pal who had been condemned to death for killing a man in a tavern brawl. In accordance with an old law of Castile, all three, when caught, were also sentenced to death. All were pardoned on condition that they enlist with Columbus, which they promptly did, and they evidently made good, as Columbus took them on his later voyages.

Columbus' plan for the voyage was simple and prac-

*Columbus sought no New World but an old one—the ancient and beautiful Orient of this 1929* Post *cover by Henry J. Soulen.*

tical. Having observed that the Portuguese navigators who went exploring west of the Azores never got anywhere, owing to the prevailing westerlies of the North Atlantic, he decided to drop down to the Canary Islands and sail thence due west before the northeast trade wind which could be counted on in the winter months, as he had observed on his African voyages. Japan, on the best map available to him, compiled according to his geographical ideas, lay due west of the Canaries, with the fabled Island of Antilia en route.

By Thursday, August 2, 1492, everything was ready for the great adventure. That night every man and boy of the fleet made his confession and communion at the Church of St. George, Palos. At a quarter to five the next morning, when the ebb tide began, the captain general—as Columbus ranked on this voyage—gave the signal to get under way. With limp sails the fleet drifted down the Rio Tinto, sailors at the long sweeps making steerageway. On the port hand they passed the convent of La Rabida as the friars were chanting the ancient hymn *Iam lucis orto sidere* with its haunting refrain *Et nunc et in perpetuum*, which we render "Evermore and evermore." Significant prophecy! For this little fleet with less than a hundred men was setting forth on a conquest for the Cross that would outlast all worldly empires.

At eight a.m., two glasses in the forenoon watch—Columbus set his watches at three, seven, and eleven o'clock—the ships were across the bar and a course was shaped for the Canaries. On the sixth day the Grand Canary could be seen above the southern horizon, but an accident to *Pinta*'s rudder delayed the fleet, repairs had to be made at Las Palmas, and it was not until September 2 that they anchored in the roadstead of San Sebastian, Gomera, westernmost inhabited island of the Canaries. Dona Beatriz de Peraza, the young and beautiful widow of the captain of Gomera, was there to receive Columbus. According to a gossipy shipmate, he fell in love with her, but he was too intent on his great project even to tarry a few days for the full moon. He took on a last load of provisions, and on September 6 weighed anchor for the last time in the Old World.

Due west was the course set by the captain general. That night they cleared the land, and by the afternoon of the ninth the high peak of Tenerife had sunk below the horizon and the three ships had an uncharted ocean to themselves.

The navigation of this voyage was very simple. Ogden Nash was about right when he wrote of Columbus:

> *Somebody show me the sunset and*
> *somebody did and he set sail for it;*
> *And he discovered America and they*
> *put him in jail for it!*

Of course, they had to hit something if they sailed due west, and for most of the way the fleet enjoyed perfect weather. It was an easy and delightful voyage, especially during the first 10 days beyond sight of land.

The wind flew fair and fresh on the starboard quarter, every sail bellied out and pulled its best, the fleet made 1,163 nautical miles westing. As they were near the northern limit of the trades, the sea was smooth, "as calm as the River of Seville," noted Columbus; and "the weather was like April in Andalusia."

There was nothing to do but freshen the nip of each rope in its block, trim the braces a yard or two, troll for dorado, and observe the dignified sea ritual of those days. Time was kept and watches changed by a sand-glass hung from a beam, which emptied every half hour, when a ship's boy reversed it and the officer of the deck or a quartermaster made a stroke on a slate. Every change of the glass and every change of watch was marked by a boy singing a traditional ditty. Every evening the boatswain piped all hands on deck for prayers. Everyone said the Lord's Prayer, Hail Mary, and the Creed, and sang the hymn "Salve Regina."

A week of dull sailing, September 19 to 26, when the wind turned soft and variable, followed the first 10 days. The men went in swimming, and the caravels were frequently rowed alongside the flagship so that the captains could consult, while the sailors shouted jokes and insults from ship to ship. In one of these conferences, toward sundown, Martin Alonzo Pinzon and Columbus were discussing a chart on which Antilia and other mythical islands were plotted, and Pinzon had just sent it back to the flagship on a line, when he rushed up on *Pinta*'s poop and shouted, "Land! Land! I claim the reward!"

There was a general scramble up the rigging and almost everyone thought he saw land on the southwestern horizon. Course was altered accordingly and all night the lookouts were on the alert. But at dawn no land was visible. It had been a cloud. To mistake a cloud on the horizon for land is a very common phenomenon at sea. It deceives sailors even nowadays, when the entire globe is charted; in those days anything was possible.

*H. W. Tilson painted Columbus' tiny ships on the wide ocean for a* Post *cover that honored Columbus Day, 1930.*

Columbus was not disturbed by this false landfall, since he reckoned that the fleet was barely two-thirds of the way to Japan. On September 20 the easterly trade wind returned. September turned into October. "God be thanked," noted Columbus, "fair wind, smooth sea, fine weather." Flying fish land on board. A boy hits a booby bird with a stone from the ballast. Martin Alonzo sails alongside and shouts something about "West by south, Japan!" Columbus doesn't quite get it. He thinks that Pinzon is trying to convey that he believes they have missed Japan. Maybe so, says the

captain general; nevertheless we shall continue west until we find land. But on October 7, when multitudes of birds were seen flying in a southwesterly direction, he changed course to west-southwest, for he knew that the Portuguese had discovered islands by taking their direction from the birds. That was wise, for the fleet was crossing the birds' route from North America to the West Indies, and their fall migration had started.

So far, this had been an unusually prosperous voyage. No squalls or gales, no gear lost, no leaks sprung, no men overboard, winds mostly fair. But it was a thrust

*After nine weeks at sea,
Columbus' men were on
the verge of mutiny.*

into the unknown, uncharted ocean, where anything might happen, toward the fabulous Japan which no European had ever seen. The sailors were now becoming discontented and mutinous, fearful they would never return. These fellows had never been more than a week's sail from land. How can we ever get back, said they, if we sail on and on and on? This Genoese is crazy; we're not sailing to the Indies, but to slow death by starvation.

The ninth and tenth days of October, when the fleet was only two or three hundred miles from the Bahamas, were the most critical of the entire voyage. "Here the people could stand it no longer," noted Columbus in his Journal, "complained of the long voyage," but (says Las Casas) "the Admiral cheered them as best he could, holding out good hope of the profit they might gain, and, he added, it was useless to complain, since he had come to sea to go to the Indies, and so would continue until he found them, with the help of Our Lord."

That little speech was the most characteristic of Columbus ever recorded. It embodies all his stubbornness, sincerity, and absolute faith in his mission. But things had gone too far for him to remedy matters by merely shouting, "Sail on! Sail on!" as Joaquin Miller has it, in that favorite old "piece" for school declamations. The two captains Pinzon, as eager to make the Indies as their captain general, were also having trouble with their crews. Evidence of what happened is conflicting, but I, for one, follow the early historian Oviedo, who spoke with many of the officers and

sailors, and had far more evidence than has come down to us. He says that Columbus, by tactful and cheery words, "awakened the courage of the weakened minds of those who were about to resort to something shameful, . . . and they agreed to do what he commanded and sail on three days and no more." This pact was made on October 10.

With only three days' grace, Columbus cracked on all the sail the ships could bear. The fleet averaged seven knots to sunset of the eleventh, when the wind increased and the sea rose. Signs of land were now abundant, and the seamen no longer complained. All night twittering birds flew overhead right on the fleet's course; by day, objects were seen that proved land to be near—a green branch with a little pink flower on it, a carved stick, a land plant. When the sun dipped under a clear horizon, every man on deck was watching for a silhouette of land against the sunset; but none was there.

On this last night, October 11-12, as it turned out to be, of the outward passage—a night big with destiny for the human race—the ships sailed as they had never sailed before, rolling and pitching in a high following sea, logging up to nine knots. The captains are pacing the high poops of their vessels, calling down testily to the helmsmen to "keep her off, damn your eyes! Let her yaw like that again and she'll broach!" Old salts are grousing and grumbling as they strain their eyes; one can imagine their conversations:

"I told the captain—and I was an able seaman when he was a little ragamuffin in Genoa—d'ye see, if you carry sail like that, captain, you'll run her under—and all he says is 'Domingo, God is protecting us!' "

"He did, did he? Well, I tell you no land is near. I don't smell none."

"You and your smeller! Here's a gold castellano says we sight land tonight."

"What do I care for your gold? We'll all be drowned if the Old Man don't take in that spritsail."

"Look at that comber r'aring up over the poop. Thank God we have a Palos man at the helm, not one of those damn Galicians."

"Look ahead, man, not astern!"

"What's the use? She's making such a roar in this sea you couldn't see breakers a cable's length ahead."

Under these circumstances, with everyone's nerves taut as the topsail sheets, there was almost certain to be a false alarm of land. At 10 p.m., an hour before moonrise, it came. Pedro Yzquierdo, Rodrigo Sanchez, and Columbus himself thought they saw a light "like a little wax candle rising and falling," but they didn't see it long, and no light was or could have been there, 35 to 40 miles off shore on a rough night. It was "all in the skipper's eye." Almost every sailor watching eagerly for an uncertain landfall at night has seen imaginary lights; and often a few shipmates will see them, too, before the illusion disappears.

Now let us get a picture of this great moment in history. It is two a.m. October 12, 1492, in the mid-watch. The moon is riding high over Orion on the port quarter, casting her light ahead. Over the western horizon hangs the great Square of Pegasus; higher and to the north, Cassiopeia's Chair; and on the starboard beam, the pole star with his Guards, the Little Dipper. A fresh gale of wind is blowing and the three vessels, *Pinta* in the lead, are rolling gunwales under, scooping up dol-

lops of green water in the waist, and throwing spray masthead high. A brave sight they are, their straining sails all silver in the moonlight, as they cut down the last thin slice of that age-old barrier between the Old World and the New.

The boy who turns the half-hour glass has just piped up:

> *Six is past and seven floweth,*
> *More shall flow if God willeth—*

when Rodrigo de Triana, on the lookout in *Pinta*, sees something like a white sand bar gleaming in the moonlight ahead, then another, and he sings out, *"Tierra! Tierra!"* Land! Land!

And this time, land it is. Captain Pinzon fires a gun to windward—the agreed signal for land—shortens sail so that the flagship can catch up, and when *Santa Maria* arrives within hailing distance, Columbus—who by this time can see the land himself—calls out: "Senor Martin Alonso, you have found land!"

To that Pinzon, remembering his earlier false land-fall, cries, "Sir, I hope I get my reward, after all!" and Columbus replies, "Yes—and 5,000 maravedis for you as a bonus!"

What they saw were the white sand cliffs on the eastern coast of the Bahamian island which the Indians called Guanahani, which Columbus named San Salvador, and the English renamed Watling's, and then San Salvador again.

*Birds were the first living creatures to welcome Columbus to the New World.*

GUERNSEY MOORE

# The Perilous Voyage of the Mayflower

## THOMAS J. FLEMING

*One of the great adventure stories of all time began in 1620 when members of the English Separatist Church returned to England from Holland where they had been living to escape religious persecution. Now their leaders had arranged for London businessmen to finance their resettlement in America. The Londoners wanted a colony in the New World; the Separatists (Puritans) wanted religious freedom.*

When the *Speedwell* docked beside the brown and gold *Mayflower* in Southampton harbor, there was an excited, happy reunion between the exiles and their leaders who had spent such difficult years in England. But these joyous greetings soon turned to consternation as the Leyden men faced some grim and unexpected facts of life.

To start with, they discovered that there were already more than 80 passengers on the *Mayflower*. These strangers, as the exiles called them, had been recruited by Thomas Weston and his London associates to fill out the colony's quota. Also on board were a number of hired hands and servants, including six children who had been picked from the thousands of orphans roaming the streets of London.

Despite these difficulties the colonists were about as ready as they would ever be. On August 5 the *Mayflower* and the *Speedwell* headed out of Southampton into the Channel, their holds filled with huge barrels of water, beer, biscuits and cod, sacks of smoked beef, and tubs of pickled eggs.

Now, however, came an almost crushing blow. Shortly after the two ships sailed, the *Speedwell* began leaking badly. She turned back for repairs in Dartmouth and then made a second start, but when the ships had crossed almost 300 miles of ocean, the *Speedwell*'s distress flag ran up again. They returned to Plymouth, where expert shipwrights reported that the ship was unseaworthy and would have to be abandoned.

This was catastrophic news. All previous colonizing expeditions had sailed in groups of two or more ships. Now, if they were to proceed at all, the voyagers would have to face the treacherous Atlantic on the *Mayflower* alone. Moreover, the *Speedwell* had been the cornerstone of their plans for fishing and trading. Without her, hopes of large profits dwindled. The colony would be isolated, with no way to get messages to England if supplies ran short.

The exiles held a conference with Captain Jones. He was confident, he said, that the *Mayflower* could make the crossing alone. After hours of prayer and meditation, the voyagers reached the courageous decision: They would go forward. Supplies were lugged from the *Speedwell* to the *Mayflower* while Jones calculated the passengers he could take from the crippled ship. Twenty of the strangers had to be left behind, but it was not difficult to find volunteers; seasickness and forebodings of disaster had taken their toll. And so, on September 6, with 102 passengers "all being compact in one ship," as William Bradford wrote, "they put to sea again."

Today, when ocean liners are the size of skyscrapers, the 113-foot *Mayflower* would seem little more than an overgrown lifeboat. Yet it was able to carry—in addition to Captain Jones, his 30 seamen, and 102 passengers—4 quartermasters, 3 master's mates, a ship's carpenter, a doctor, a cook, and gunners to man the ship's 10 cannon.

No one knows exactly how the voyagers were arranged, but there have been educated guesses. Some historians believe Captain Jones and his mates bunked in the poop house, giving up their cabins to the passengers. Most of the married couples, the unmarried girls, and youngest children probably lived in these officers' cab-

*The Mayflower was little more than half the size of this galleon of the same period.*

JOHN CECIL CLAY 1899

ins, while the single men and grown boys stayed on the gun deck, just above the ship's deep hold.

The lack of privacy and crowded quarters must have been painful, but these problems were overshadowed by the unpalatable food—typical of ships of the time. The basic diet was cold fish or meat, pickled in brine, and served with beer and saucer-size biscuits. The women may have occasionally made stew or soup—welcome treats because the diners then had something to soften the biscuits, which became as hard as cannonballs.

For the exiles from Leyden, however, the overcrowded conditions and wretched food were of less concern than the future organization of their colony. Acutely aware that they were now a minority—a mere 27 adults—they knew they would have to find allies among the strangers if they were to retain control of the group and establish the kind of commonwealth they envisioned.

Two men immediately impressed the exiles. One was a blond, husky 21-year-old cooper named John Alden. By royal command, every ship clearing an English port had to have a cooper aboard to keep the barrels of beer and water tight. The other man was Miles Standish, a short, redheaded former captain in Queen Elizabeth's army who had been signed to handle the colony's defenses. When the first bouts with seasickness were over, Standish began drilling squads of men, teaching them to handle the swords and matchlock muskets that had been bought for the expedition. Although he stood

little more than five feet tall, Standish was a born leader who easily kept discipline among the men.

But the drills on deck could not last for long. Each day Captain Jones scanned the northwest horizon, grimly watching for the heavy weather that could be expected when the autumn westerlies blew in from Greenland. Finally it came—the cold breath of the Arctic, tearing down the long reach of whitecapped sea.

Hatches were secured and portholes bolted tight as the huge waves—some as high as 50 feet—stormed over every inch of the *Mayflower*'s decks. Now there was nothing the captain could do but "hull"—let the ship run before the wind with bare masts, even though it was being driven hundreds of miles off course.

Still the waves came, great smashing blows of the Atlantic's inexhaustible fist. Belowdecks the frightened passengers huddled together and prayed. With every wave, freezing water cascaded down upon them, for the pounding seas had opened seams in the ship's upper works. In the foul semidarkness someone suggested a psalm, and they began to sing. But another monstrous wave hit, and with a tremendous crash a main beam amidship cracked and buckled.

Now there was pandemonium. The captain and mates rushed to the gun deck to stare at the sagging beam and the splintered deck around it. Water gushed through new openings. Nothing would save the ship unless the beam could be forced back in place. The strongest men aboard put their shoulders to the job, but the massive beam only sagged more. Then someone remembered a "great iron screw" brought along for house-raising in the New World. Sailors scrambled into the hold, lugged the screw up to the deck, and placed it under the cracked timber. Slowly, twisting the crank, they raised the beam into place again.

For days and days the *Mayflower* wallowed through mountainous seas.

By now the passengers had been living in the foul darkness belowdecks for weeks—a hundred people crowded into a space not much roomier than a small house. They had been unable to change clothes or wash for over two months. Sanitary facilities were simply buckets. The food was getting worse every day.

But now came a new crisis—cries of pain from the Great Cabin. Elizabeth Hopkins, one of the strangers, was in labor. Neither she nor her husband, Stephen Hopkins, had ever expected to have their child during an Atlantic gale, and at William Brewster's suggestion the exiles and strangers knelt together in prayer for a safe delivery. Soon afterward there was good news—a lusty, yowling baby boy had been born. Stephen Hopkins promptly named him Oceanus.

The birth cheered everyone until, as the tenth week drew to a close, William Butten, a husky, 22-year-old servant, fell ill. It was the first case of scurvy, and it was fatal. The sailors sewed the body into a shroud and sent it plunging into the sea. Belowdecks there were ominous signs of more disease. Men and women were complaining of swollen legs, chills, and fever. Fortunately the weather at last began to clear. Hatches were opened, and, on the captain's advice, even those who were sick went on deck for exercise.

Now an air of expectancy raced through the ship; Captain Jones had reported that landfall could come at any time. Aloft in the crow's nest a lookout peered endlessly over the western horizon, but he saw nothing more than miles of trackless ocean. Another day passed. Would it ever end?

On the morning of November 9 the crew plodded through their routines as Captain Jones watched the dawn grow on the glistening sea. Above, the sails flapped in a dying wind. Mate John Clark pointed to the changing color of the water—indigo blue had turned to emerald. Then from the maintop lookout burst the cry that passengers and crew had been hearing in their dreams for weeks.

"La-and Ho! La-and Ho!"

There were shouts of joy and tears of relief. Many feel on their knees and thanked God with simple spontaneity. After consulting his charts Captain Jones reported that the long, low, sand-covered shore they were approaching was part of that great arm of land known as Cape Cod.

*In spring the* Mayflower *returned to England, leaving the small group of settlers alone—and lonely—on the New World's shore.*

*If Bligh was the villain of* Mutiny on the Bounty, *he was the hero of its sequel* Men Against the Sea. *Painting by George Gibbs.*

# Men Against the Sea

## BY CHARLES NORDHOFF
## AND JAMES NORMAN HALL

*World War I fliers who served in France with the Lafayette Escadrille, Nordhoff and Hall shared a love of adventure, ships, and the sea. After the war they lived in Tahiti—once Otaheite—and there wrote* Mutiny on the Bounty. *Two sequels,* Men Against the Sea *and* Pitcairn's Island, *first appeared as serials in the* Post. *These are fictionalized accounts of historical events;* Men Against the Sea *is based on a log Bligh kept during the 48-day voyage to Timor in the Dutch East Indies.*

On the morning of April 28, 1789, the *Bounty* was running before a light easterly breeze, within view of the island of Tofoa, in the Friendly Archipelago. I was awakened a little after daybreak by Charles Churchill, the master-at-arms, and John Mills, the gunner's mate, who informed me that the ship had been seized by Fletcher Christian, the lieutenant, and the greater part of the ship's company, and that I was to go on deck at once. These men were of Christian's party. Churchill was armed with pistols and Mills with a musket. I dressed in great haste and was then marched to the upper deck. It will be understood with what amazement I looked about me. To be aroused from a quiet sleep to find the ship filled with armed men and Captain Bligh a prisoner, so shocked and stupefied me that, at first, I could scarcely accept the evidence of my eyes.

There was nothing to be done. The mutineers were in complete possession of the ship, and those who they knew would remain loyal to their commander were so carefully guarded as to preclude all possibility of resistance. I was ordered to stand by the mainmast with William Elphinstone, master's mate, and John Norton, one of the quartermasters. Two of the seamen, armed with muskets, the bayonets fixed, were stationed over us, and I well remember one of them, John Williams, saying to me: "Stand ye there, Mr. Ledward. We mean ye no harm, but by God, we'll run ye through the guts if ye make a move toward Captain Bligh!" Elphinstone, Norton, and I tried to recall these men to their senses, but their minds were so inflamed by hatred toward Captain Bligh that nothing we could say made the least impression upon them. He showed great resolution, and, although they threatened him repeatedly, he outfaced the ruffians and dared them to do their worst.

I had been standing by the mainmast only a short time when Christian, who had been chief of those guarding Mr. Bligh, gave this business into the charge of Churchill and four or five others, that he might hasten the work of sending the loyal men out of the ship. It was only then that we learned what his plans were, and we had no time to reflect upon the awful consequences to us of his cruelty and folly. The ship was in an uproar, and it was a near thing that Bligh was not murdered where he stood. It had been the plan of the mutineers to set us adrift in the small cutter, but her bottom was so rotten that they were at last persuaded to let us have the launch, and men were now set to work clearing her that she might be swung over the side. Whilst this was being done, I caught Christian's eye, and he came forward to where I stood.

"Mr. Ledward, you may stay with the ship if you choose," he said.

"I shall follow Captain Bligh," I replied. . . .

I well remember the silence that seemed to flow in upon our little company directly we had been cast adrift—the wide silence of mid-ocean, accentuated by the faint creaking of the oars against the tholepins. We rowed six oars in the launch, but were so deeply laden that we made slow progress toward the island of Tofoa, to the northeast of us, and distant about 10 leagues. Fryer sat at the tiller. Captain Bligh, Mr. Nelson, Elphinstone, the master's mate, and Peckover, the gunner, were all seated in the stern sheets. The rest of us were crowded on the thwarts in much the same positions as those we had taken upon coming into the launch. Bligh was half turned in his seat, gazing somberly after the distant vessel; nor, during the next hour, I

think, did he once remove his eyes from her. He appeared to have forgotten the rest of us, nor did any of us speak to remind him of our presence. Our thoughts were as gloomy as his own, and we felt as little inclined to express them.

My sympathy went out to Mr. Bligh in this hour of bitter disappointment; I could easily imagine how appalling the ruin of his plans must have appeared to him at a time when he had every expectation of completing them to the last detail. We had been homeward bound, the mission of our long voyage—that of collecting breadfruit plants in Otaheite to be carried to the West Indies—successfully accomplished. This task, entrusted to his care by His Majesty's government through the interest of his friend and patron, Sir Joseph Banks, had deeply gratified him, and well indeed had he justified that trust. Now, in a moment, his sanguine hopes were brought to nothing. His ship was gone; his splendid charts of coasts and islands were gone as well, and he had nothing to show for all the long months of careful and painstaking labor. He found himself cast adrift with 18 of his company in his own ship's launch, with no more than a compass, a sextant, and his journal, in

*Rough men used to settling disputes with their fists—as in this 1905 illustration by N. C. Wyeth—made up the Bounty's crew.*

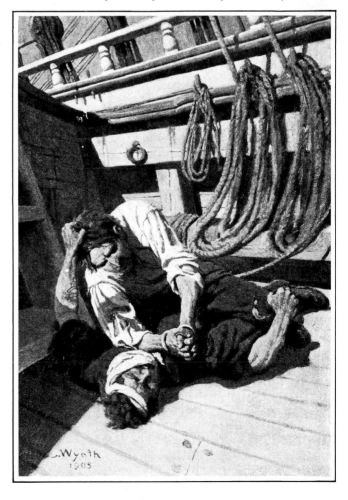

*Captain Bligh and his 18 men in the* Bounty's launch, *a 1933 illustration by Anton Otto Fischer for* Men Against the Sea.

the midst of the greatest of oceans and thousands of miles from any place where he could look for help. Small wonder if, at that time, he felt the taste of dust and ashes in his mouth.

For an hour we moved slowly on toward Tofoa, the most northwesterly of the islands comprising the Friendly Archipelago. This group had been so christened by Captain Cook, but our experiences among its inhabitants, only a few days before the mutiny, led us to believe that Cook must have called them "friendly" in a spirit of irony. They are a virile race, but we had found them savage and treacherous in the extreme, as different as could be imagined from the natives of Otaheite. Only the possession of firearms had saved us from being attacked and overcome whilst we were engaged in wooding and watering on the island of Annamooka.

Tofoa we had not visited, and as I gazed at the faint blue outline on the horizon, I tried, with little success, to convince myself that our experiences there might be more fortunate.

Many an anxious glance was turned in Captain Bligh's direction, but for an hour at least he remained in the same position, gazing after the distant ship. When at length he turned away, it was never to look toward her again. He now took charge of his new command with an assurance, a quiet cheerfulness that heartened us all. He first set us to work to bring some order into the boat. We were, as I have said, desperately crowded, but when we had stored away our supplies we had elbowroom at least. Our first care was, of course, to take stock of our provisions. We found that we had sixteen pieces of pork each weighing about two pounds; three bags of bread of fifty pounds each, six quarts of rum, six bottles of wine, and twenty-eight gallons of water in three ten-gallon kegs. We also had four empty barricos, each capable of holding eight gallons. The carpenter, Purcell, had succeeded in fetching away one of his tool chests, although the mutineers had removed many of the tools before allowing it to be handed down. Our remaining supplies, outside of personal belongings, consisted of my medicine chest, the launch's two lugsails, some spare canvas, two or three coils of rope, and a copper pot, together with some odds and ends of boat's gear which the boatswain had had the forethought to bring with him.

To show how deeply laden we were, it is enough to say that my hand, as it rested on the gunwale, was repeatedly wet with drops of water from the small waves that licked along the sides of the boat. Fortunately, the sea was calm and the sky held a promise of good weather, at least for a sufficient time to enable us to reach Tofoa.

Reliefs at the oars were changed every hour, each of us taking his turn. Gradually the blue outline of the island became more distinct, and by the middle of the afternoon we had covered well over half the distance to it. About this time the faint breeze freshened and came round to the southeast, which enabled us to get up one of our lugsails. Captain Bligh now took the tiller and we altered our course to fetch the northern side of the island.

I now cast about in my mind, trying to anticipate what Captain Bligh's plan for us might be. Our only hope of succor would lie in the colonies in the Dutch East Indies, but they were so far distant that the prospect of reaching one of them seemed fantastic. I thought of Otaheite, where we could be certain of kindly treatment on the part of the Indians, but that island was all of 1,200 miles distant and directly to windward. In view of these circumstances, Mr. Bligh would never attempt a return there.

Meanwhile, we proceeded on our way under a sky whose serenity seemed to mock at the desperate plight of the men in the tiny boat crawling beneath it. The sun dipped into the sea behind us, and in the light that streamed up from beyond the horizon Tofoa stood out in clear relief. We estimated the peak of its central mountain to be about 2,000 feet high. It was a volcano, and a thin cloud of vapor hung above it, taking on a saffron color in the afterglow.

*Bligh's men go ashore on Tofoa but they find only meager supplies of food and water and are attacked by unfriendly natives. At sea again, they discuss the possibility of reaching the Dutch settlement at Timor. The winds are favorable at this time of year, Bligh says, and the launch seaworthy.*

"As to the perils we must meet"—Bligh paused, and then went on—"of those I need not speak. They are known to all of you. But this I will say: If we are to reach Timor we must live upon a daily allowance of food and water no more than sufficient to preserve our lives. I desire every man's assurance that he will cheerfully agree to the amount I shall decide upon. It will be small indeed, but we can be almost certain of replenishing our water many times before the end of the voyage. However, that remains to be seen, and I shall not anticipate doing so in deciding what each man's portion shall be. . . . Mr. Fryer, have I your solemn promise to abide by my judgment in this matter?"

"Yes, sir," Fryer replied promptly.

Mr. Bligh then called each man by name and all agreed as Fryer had done.

These matters having been decided, we fell silent, and so remained for some time; then Cole, who was seated amidships, said: "Mr. Bligh, we should be pleased if you would ask God's blessing upon our voyage."

"That I shall do, Mr. Cole," Bligh replied.

Never, I imagine, have English seamen been more sensible of the need for Divine guidance than the eighteen men in the *Bounty*'s launch. We waited, our heads bowed in the darkness, for our leader to speak.

"Almighty God, Thou seest our afflictions. Thou knowest our need. Grant that we may quit ourselves like men in the trials and dangers that lie before us. Watch over us. Strengthen our hearts; and in Thy divine mercy and compassion, bring us all in safety to the haven toward which we now direct our course. Amen."

*Bligh's determination to see the mutineers punished helped him survive the 4,000-mile voyage to Timor in the Dutch East Indies.*

DRAWN BY F. R. GRUGER AND JAMES PRESTON

# Around the World Alone

## BY JOSHUA SLOCUM

*In 1895, Slocum was a 51-year-old retired merchant captain—retired because the ship he owned had been wrecked and he had no money to buy another. A New Bedford friend offered Slocum the beached shell of a 37-foot sloop and, because he was homesick for the sea, he repaired her, rigged her for deep-sea sailing, and named her the* Spray. *She was a sturdy and lucky craft, for Slocum set out to sea in her and returned eventually to write a book called* Sailing Alone Around the World. *In this excerpt, Slocum tells about stormy Cape Horn, and about an encounter with unfriendly natives.*

The *Spray*'s good luck followed fast. As she sailed along through a labyrinth of islands, I discovered that she was in Cockburn Channel, which leads into the Strait of Magellan at a point opposite Cape Froward, and that she was already passing Thieves' Bay, suggestively named. And at night, March 8, she was at anchor in a snug cove at the Turn!

Every heartbeat on the *Spray* now counted thanks.

Here I pondered on the events of the last few days, and, strangely enough, instead of feeling rested from sitting or lying down, I now began to feel jaded and worn; but a hot meal of venison stew soon put me right, so that I could sleep. As drowsiness came on I sprinkled the deck with tacks, and then I turned in, bearing in mind the advice of my old friend Samblich that I was not to step on them myself. I saw to it carefully that most of them stood point up; for when the *Spray* passed Thieves' Bay two canoes put out and followed in her wake, and there was no disguising the fact any longer that I was alone.

Now, it is well known that one cannot step on a tack without saying something about it. A pretty good Christian will whistle when he steps on the sharp end of a carpet tack; a savage will howl and claw the air, and that was just what happened that night about twelve o'clock, while I was asleep in the cabin, where the savages thought they had the better of me, sloop and all, but changed their minds when they stepped on deck, for then they thought that I or somebody else had them. I had no need of a dog; they howled like a pack of hounds. I had hardly use for a gun. They jumped pell-mell, some into their canoes and some into the sea, and there was a deal of free language over it as they went. I fired several guns when I came on deck, to let the rascals know that I was at home, and then I turned in again, feeling sure I should not be disturbed any more by people who left in such a great hurry. . . .

On the morning of the 9th, after a refreshing rest and a warm breakfast, and after I had swept up the tacks, I got out what spare canvas there was on board, and began to sew the pieces together in the shape of a peak for my square mainsail, the tarpaulin. The day promised fine weather and light winds but appearances in Tierra del Fuego do not always count. While I was wondering why no trees grew on the slope abreast of the anchorage, half minded to lay by the sail-making and go on shore with my gun and in-spect a white boulder

on the beach near the brook, a williwaw came down with such terrific force as to carry the *Spray*, with two anchors down, out of the cove and away into deep water. No wonder trees did not grow on the side of that hill. Great Boreas! a tree would need to be all roots to hold on against such a furious wind.

From the cove to the nearest land to leeward was a long drift, however,

*Slocum's* Spray *would have appeared toy-size beside the tall clippers still to be seen at sea in his day. By Gordon Grant.*

and I had ample time to weigh both anchors before the sloop came near any danger, and so no harm came of it. I saw no more savages that day or the next; they probably had some sign by which they knew of the coming williwaws; at least, they were wise in not being afloat even on the second day, for I had no sooner gotten to work at sail-making again, after the anchor was down, than the wind, as on the day before, picked the sloop up and flung her seaward with a vengeance, anchor and all, as before. This fierce wind, usual to the Magellan country, continued on through the day, and swept the sloop by several miles of steep bluffs and precipices overhanging a bold shore of unusually wild and uninviting appearance. I kept on sailing in hope, since I had no choice but to go on, heading across for St. Nicholas Bay, where I had cast anchor February 19. It was now the 10th of March! Upon reaching the bay the second time I had circumnavigated the wildest part of desolate Tierra del Fuego. The sea was turbulent, and by the merest accident the *Spray* saved her bones from the rocks, coming into the bay. The parting of a staysail sheet in a williwaw, when she was plunging into the storm, brought me forward to see instantly a dark cliff ahead and breakers so close under the bows that I felt surely lost, and in my thoughts cried, "Is the hand of fate against me, after all, leading me in the end to this dark spot?" I sprang aft again, unheeding the flapping sail, and threw the wheel over, expecting, as the sloop came down into the hollow of a wave, to feel her timbers smash under me on the rocks. But at the touch of her helm she swung clear, and in the next moment was in the lee of the land.

It was the small island in the middle of the bay for which the sloop had been steering, and which she made with such unerring aim as nearly to run it down. Farther along in the bay was the anchorage, which I managed to reach, but before I could get the anchor down another squall caught the sloop and whirled her round like a top and carried her away, to leeward of the bay. Still farther to leeward was a great headland, and I bore off for that. This was retracing my course toward Sandy Point, for the gale was from the southwest.

I had the sloop soon under good control, however, and in a short time rounded to under the lee of a

GEORGE GIBBS

mountain, where the sea was as smooth as a millpond, and the sails flapped and hung limp while she carried her way close in. Here I thought I would anchor and rest till morning, the depth being eight fathoms very close to the shore. But it was interesting to see, as I let go the anchor, that it did not reach bottom before another williwaw struck down from this mountain and carried the sloop off faster than I could pay out cable. Therefore, instead of resting, I had to heave up the anchor with 50 fathoms of cable hanging up and down in deep water. This was in that part of the strait called Famine Reach. Dismal Famine Reach! On the sloop's crab-windlass I worked the rest of the night.

It was daybreak when the anchor was at the hawse. By this time the wind had gone down, and cat's-paw took the place of williwaws, while the sloop drifted slowly toward Sandy Point. She came within sight of ships at anchor in the roads, and I was more than half minded to put in for new sails, but the wind coming out from the northeast, which was fair for the other direction, I turned the prow of the *Spray* westward once more for the Pacific, to traverse a second time the second half of my first course through the strait.

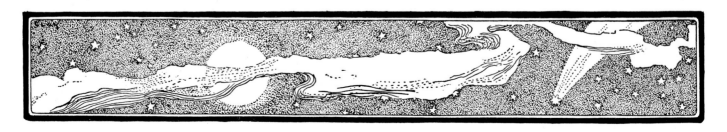

# "We Need Help!" Radioed the Titanic

## BY CAPTAIN SIR ARTHUR ROSTRON

*The liner* Californian *was the ship closest to the* Titanic *that night, but the* Californian's *radio operator had closed down his receiver and gone to bed. In a 1927* Post *article Captain Rostron tells what happened aboard the ship that did receive the urgent message that was tapped out by the* Titanic's *radio operator, Harold Bride.*

**M**y ship, the *Carpathia*, left New York, April 11, 1912, bound for Gibraltar, Genoa, Naples, and other Mediterranean ports. We had on board 120 first-class passengers, 50 second-class, and 560 third-class. Harold Thomas Cottam, a young man barely past his majority, was in charge of our wireless apparatus, which had a sending radius of about 250 miles. He was the only operator we carried. Around midnight of the following Sunday, Cottam was making preparations to turn in for the night. He had taken off his coat, but lingered at his instruments for a few moments to get an answer to some message from the steamship *Parisian*, with which he had been in communication. While waiting he determined to call the *Titanic* to ask her operator if he knew that Cape Cod had a batch of messages for his ship.

"Come at once; we need help," was the astounding answer which came back to Cottam. It was incredible to him that of all the vessels on the ocean this particular one should be calling for aid. Not only was she the largest ship which had ever taken to the water, with a gross tonnage of 45,000 and an overall length of 882 feet, 6 inches, but she was at that moment making her maiden trip from England to the United States. She carried a total of more than 2,200 people, and in her cabins were many persons of international note, including Mr. and Mrs. John Jacob Astor; Major Archibald Butts, military aid to President Taft; William T. Stead, the Irish journalist and author; Charles M. Hays, president of the Grand Trunk Railway System; and John B. Thayer, vice-president of the Pennsylvania Railroad. The *Titanic* at that moment was the world's foremost steamship. New York was waiting to welcome her as the queen of the seas.

"Shall I report to the captain?" Cottam asked.

"Yes," the *Titanic* operator replied.

Cottam telephoned the bridge and spoke to the senior officer in charge. It was then about half-past twelve in the early morning, and I was asleep in my

*Lifebelts and lifeboats of the* Titanic's *time.*

cabin. The senior officer ran down the companionway to awaken me. His manner was brisk and official.

"We have just received a CQD from the *Titanic*, sir," he reported.

I rubbed my eyes and looked at him questioningly. "From the *Titanic*—are you quite sure it's from the *Titanic*?"

"Quite sure, sir."

"Have you her bearings?"

"Yes, sir."

I hurried into a few clothes and hastened to the bridge. Twice I asked Cottam if he were certain that he had received the message correctly, it all seemed so unbelievable. He replied he was positive.

"Give them our position and tell them we are coming as fast as we can," I directed. Cottam sent the message off immediately and then got in touch with the *Baltic* and *Olympic*, which were within the range of our wireless. The last message he got from the *Titanic* was that her engine room was filling fast. She was going down by the head.

When I reached the decision to go to the assistance of the *Titanic*, which was the moment I learned of her peril, I realized there might be some risk to the *Carpathia* in the field of icebergs which we should undoubtedly have to penetrate. The thought of not going did not present itself. We were badly needed, and I was sure our passengers would have decided the way I did, if the question had been put to them. It was one of those problems the captain of a ship must solve instantly and upon his own initiative. He is in supreme command.

The position of the *Titanic* was 41:46 north latitude, 50:14 west longitude. Our own bearings showed us we were 58 miles away from her. We quickly charted our course and pointed our nose to the spot where the great liner was slowly sinking. I sent for the chief engineer, told him what had happened, and gave instructions to put on an extra force of stokers. He ran below to see that these orders were carried out. We proceeded under forced draft, with every ounce of steam conserved to increase our speed. It was a bitterly cold night, but we even shut off the steam from the radiators throughout the ship in order that the boilers would generate their greatest power. The *Carpathia*'s normal speed was 14½ knots. She got up to 16 and at times 17 under the bleeding to which she was subjected on this occasion. The weather was clear and the sea oily.

As soon as we had turned around and started on our way, I instructed the first officer to knock off the usual

*"To the boats!" Anton Otto Fischer painted this action-filled 1910 illustration.*

Monday work and to prepare the lifeboats so that they would be ready for immediate use upon our arrival. Then I sent for the heads of the various other departments—the doctor, the purser, and the chief steward. I directed the English doctor and his assistants to take charge of the first-class dining room, the Italian doctor and his assistants the second-class dining room, and the Hungarian doctor and his assistants the third-class dining room. They were ordered to have stimulants and medical supplies on hand, together with hot coffee and blankets, which the chief steward would furnish.

Stewards were stationed at the different gangways through the ship to hold back our own passengers and to reassure them if they became alarmed. As it turned out, this precaution was unnecessary. Only two of the *Carpathia*'s passengers knew that we had altered our course and what had happened. They were cautioned to strict silence, and respected our wishes, knowing that it would seriously impede the work of rescue if the decks were cluttered with our own passengers and if

*The hornlike structures on the deck of a* Titanic-*era liner were ventilators.*

our crew had to contend with any excitement or disorder. Nearly everybody had retired for the night, and many of them were still asleep hours after we had reached the scene, unaware that they had played an unconscious part in the tragedy.

The purser and his assistants were ordered to receive the *Titanic*'s survivors at the gangway, obtain their Christian names and surnames, and to send the list to land by wireless as quickly as possible. While we were on our way, everybody not concerned in the navigation of the ship turned to making ready the various public rooms for the reception of the survivors. We had no idea how many there might be. As each officer finished the task assigned him he so reported. About 30 minutes before we reached the *Titanic*'s position, everything aboard the *Carpathia* was in readiness.

After seeing that these things were being done, I went to the bridge and stayed there. There were three officers continually on the bridge—one man in the crow's nest and two in the eyes of the ship. At quarter past two o'clock I gave the order that rockets be fired at intervals of every 15 minutes that they might be seen by those aboard the *Titanic*, if she was still afloat, or by her survivors in the lifeboats, if she had sunk. At twenty minutes to three I saw a flare half a point on the quarter bow and supposed it to be the *Titanic*. I was relieved to think that she was still afloat, but this reassurance was of short duration. The flare had presumably come from one of the lifeboats.

Soon afterward I made out icebergs one point on the port bow. We had been passing them continually for some time, but it was not until daylight came that we realized what a large nest of them there was. They were all around us. I could make out at least 20 which projected from 150 to 200 feet above the water, together with a number of smaller ones. In the vicinity were also numerous growlers—large lumps of ice which had broken away from the bergs in the warmer temperature of the water into which they had drifted. The miracle of it was that we had missed these bergs. Providence had intervened to spare the *Carpathia* while she was bleeding herself on this errand of help.

It was about quarter after four o'clock when the *Carpathia*'s engines stopped. I looked at my chart to see what the depth of the water was. We were in 2,000 fathoms. The first lifeboat came alongside within ten minutes. By the time we got her occupants aboard ship it was daybreak and we could see the remaining fourteen lifeboats, all within a radius of four miles. The only trace of the *Titanic* herself was wreckage which strewed the waters.

# Try Building a Chinese Junk

## BY RICHARD HALLIBURTON

*Princeton-educated, with the poise and manners of a diplomat, the stamina of a channel swimmer, and the blond good looks of a Greek God,*

*Richard Halliburton made a profession of adventuring. He climbed mountains; he flew around the world when aviation was in its infancy; he swam, sailed, rode camelback over the desert. He visited all the out-of-the-way corners of the world, and he made a good living by lecturing and writing books about his exploits. Halliburton was born at the turn of the century and he was not yet 40 when he arrived in Hong Kong to begin his last adventure, sailing a Chinese junk across the Pacific to the Golden Gate International Exhibition. He wrote this account for a newspaper syndicate to publish in the United States.*

It was seeing a schooner—years ago—with its great wings spread, sailing out through the Golden Gate at San Francisco, that first made me want to go to sea. My heart went straight aboard her, and, until this day, it's never come back—for long.

I spent several years in wandering by sea and land, visiting all the nice warm countries on the map. These travels at last brought me to China. And in the harbor of Foochow I found my first true love again—ships with sails. Not just one or a dozen, but scores and hundreds. The harbor was alive with sails.

These ships, this time, were not schooners—something far more wonderful and exciting than that. Nor were they yachts or yawls, sloops or luggers, barks or barkentines. They were *junks*. And they had, for me, an immediate and tremendous appeal. No ship I'd ever seen before had such glorious bright-colored sails as these Chinese craft, or such carved, up-soaring castles on the poops, or such gay and gaudy dragon-pictures on the sterns.

A Chinese junk! Always, in my mind, this meant a ramshackle, unwieldy, unseaworthy scow, slogging along, and manned by laundrymen. Such dismal ignorance! Junks have beauty, grace, and glamour. In Foochow they were all adorned with banners, and gleamed with oil and paint. They bristled with cast-iron cannon. On their mast-tops sparkled gilded good-luck charms. Their three batwing sails, made of shining yellow mats, drove them over the water with the ease of a flying sea gull.

Then and there I resolved to buy one at the first opportunity, and sail it up and down the Seven Seas.

And now the opportunity has come. As I write, I'm on my way back to China with a group of American comrades, to buy a junk just like the gaudy graceful ships I saw in Foochow.

The name? I chose that long ago—the *Sea Dragon*. On the day of launching, the prettiest Chinese girl whom I can find will break a bottle of rice wine on the *Sea Dragon*'s nose. And as the junk slides down the ways we'll all beat gongs and shoot off firecrackers, in proper Chinese fashion, to drive away the demons of storm and shipwreck. . . .

*Unfortunately, no junk large and sturdy enough to cross the Pacific was available for purchase, and Halliburton undertook to have one built. Five months later he sent off this report on his activities:*

If any one of my readers wishes to be driven rapidly insane, and doesn't know how to go about it, let me make a suggestion: Try building a Chinese junk in a Chinese shipyard, during a war with Japan. From personal experience I know this to be a most effective method. In fact I don't see how it can fail.

From the hour I signed a contract, here in Hong Kong, with Mr. Fat Kau, to build me a beautiful junk—"big, but not *too* big; colorful, but not garish"—until today, when my *Sea Dragon* is ready to sail, I've been through so many shipbuilding battles, and been so plagued by the superlative perversity of Chinese carpenters, that I'm a mental wreck. Nothing that can happen on our voyage to San Francisco can possibly upset me now.

We wished our junk to be designed, constructed, and decorated in strict accordance with native custom—and the work must be done by natives. One shipbuilder, Mr. Fat Kau, was recommended above all others. So we picked an interpreter and went to interview him.

The tram carried us along the mountain-framed shore, away from downtown Hong Kong, past the British barracks, farther and farther into the squalid Chinese waterfront slums. Opposite a high-smelling soy sauce factory, and between the Peachy Garage and a Gentleman's Parlor for Beauty was the place where junks are born.

Mr. Fat Kau welcomed us graciously. We were clearly a group of foreign idiots . . . wanting to build a junk and name it the *Sea Dragon* and sail it to San Francisco, 9,000 miles away. But we were cash customers, so the generous man agreed, finally, to accept only twice what we offered. When we departed, we had a contract, beautifully sealed in red with Kau's private *chop*, and the *Sea Dragon*—we imagined—was as good as built.

From that day to this, the cramped little shipyard has been a sort of hired private madhouse for John Welch, our captain; for Henry von Fehren, our engineer; and for me. The *Sea Dragon* is now ready to sail, and I have no doubt it is a sound, seaworthy ship; but I have no doubt, either, that its construction violated every accepted rule of shipbuilding known to man.

First there was the keel, a magnificent log of jacalwood, 60 feet long. A sawmill could have squared it off in 20 minutes. I soon realized that, with Chinese methods, this same job would take a week. The carpenters hacked at it with little axes, and sawed it by hand. When I was ready to tear up the contract because of the

*The junk had fore-and-aft rigging, centerboard, and stern rudder long before European ships. By Anthony Cucchi.*

lack of progress, the workmen smiled blandly and reminded me that the Chinese have been hand-cutting their keels for 4,000 years.

Once the keel was laid, one might suppose the ribs would follow, and then they would be covered by planks to make the hull. In any sensible shipyard this would be the sequence. But not in Fat Kau's! He put on the planks *without* any ribs, suspending them from bamboo ropes, propping them up with bamboo poles. "How can you tell where the ribs should go, unless you have the planking up first?" he asked. In other words, "How do you know where to put the frame of a house until you have the walls up and the roof on?"

I groaned at this demented idea—but again got the "4,000 years" argument.

Next morning as I approached the shipyard I saw a cloud of flame and smoke pouring out of it. *There*, I felt sure, went my expensive hand-sawn keel, and all the laboriously gathered timbers for our junk. In the greatest alarm I dashed through the gate. The smoke all but choked me, but nobody except me seemed in any way concerned by the conflagration. Through the murk I presently saw that it was my three-inch teak hull-planking (worth its weight in radium at such times as these) going up in flames. Such criminal, stupid carelessness! Such indifference to my burning planks . . . and the wartime blockade! . . . *How* would I get more? . . . Why were the Chinese such infuriating fools!

In another moment I realized that the fires had a purpose. Each teak plank—twenty feet long—was stretched across two wooden sawhorses six feet apart. A heavy cast-iron cannon weighed down each end. Between the sawhorses a bonfire had been built, which heated the wood to combustion point. Whenever it actually burst into flames, a Chinese boy spat a mouthful of water on the burning spot. The heat charred the plank an inch deep, but (with the aid of the weights on the ends) bent the thick plank into a crescent. When the timber cooled off, it retained its shape, and thus fitted the curved lines of the hull. Indeed, exclaimed Mr. Fat Kau, how else would you do it?

Soon after this crisis had passed we had another one to face. I came to the yard to find all the carpenters on a sit-down strike. Their wages had been paid; so far as I knew they had absolutely no grievance.

But apparently I didn't know much. They were striking because I had failed to give them a party. Every self-respecting workman in China expects the employer to give two big parties per job—one at the beginning, one when the work is finished. And we had given no party at all. We were guilty of the worst possible manners. So perhaps a sit-down strike would teach us the customs of the country.

There were something like 50 men on the job at the time. Our interpreter estimated it would cost thirty Hong Kong dollars—about nine dollars American—to give them all a whooping big blowout. "But don't give the money to Number One Wife," he cautioned. "She will give only twenty-dollar party and keep the difference." So we turned the money over to Number Four Wife who was supposed to be less grasping. And when she had finished cajoling, intimidating, and generally wearing down the shopkeepers, she proudly spread a feast that would have cost anyone else in Hong Kong a cool hundred. There were barrels and baskets of Chinese food. The rice wine would almost have floated our *Sea Dragon*. There were girls and music. In no time at all everybody was tipsy. And then—the climax of the evening—they all helped themselves to opium. Without the opium, so I was told, no party was worth being invited to.

I watched each of the 50 guests smoke his fill of the drug. Then, toward dawn, they climbed up onto the unfinished ribs and scaffolding of the *Sea Dragon* and went to sleep.

Next day the men returned to work with redoubled energy, and the pounding, sawing, and nailing could be heard from afar.

When not occupied with strikes, parties, and building problems, I sometimes found time to enjoy the pageant of the shipyard. It was wholly, hopelessly Chinese. It sprawled along the waterfront in a wild confusion of timbers, bamboo poles, babies, old cannon, cooking fires, carpenters, and wives. Hens roosted on the big two-man saws. Tailless cats prowled, slant-eyed, among the logs of teak and camphorwood. Cached in every cranny were the workmen's bedrolls—for all the workmen sleep at the job at night. "Job" and "home" are synonymous in the Chinese laborer's lexicon.

Our ship grew by spurts and whims.

*The* Sea Dragon *was completed early in 1939 but she didn't handle well, rolling very badly in rough water. On a first try for San Francisco one crewman broke an ankle, another became ill. They turned back, replaced the men, and gave the ship an extra keel to make it more stable. They sailed, finally, on March 3. Two days later a radio message placed the* Sea Dragon *halfway to Midway Island but wallowing in high seas. There was no further word; no trace of junk or crew was ever found.*

The Only
Way to
Travel

# The Rough Crossing

## A STORY BY F. SCOTT FITZGERALD

Once on the long, covered piers, you have come into a ghostly country that is no longer Here and not yet There. Especially at night. There is a hazy yellow vault full of shouting, echoing voices. There is the rumble of trucks and the clump of trunks, the strident chatter of a crane and the first salt smell of the sea. You hurry through, even though there's time. The past, the continent, is behind you; the future is that glowing mouth in the side of the ship; this dim turbulent alley is too confusedly the present.

Up the gangplank, and the vision of the world adjusts itself, narrows. One is a citizen of a commonwealth smaller than Andorra. One is no longer so sure of anything. Curiously unmoved the men at the purser's desk, cell-like the cabin, disdainful the eyes of voyagers and their friends, solemn the officer who stands on the deserted promenade deck thinking something of his own as he stares at the crowd below. A last odd idea that one didn't really have to come, then the loud, mournful whistles, and the thing—certainly not a boat, but rather a human idea, a frame of mind—pushes forth into the big dark night.

Adrian Smith, one of the celebrities on board—not actually a very great celebrity, but important enough to

be bathed in flashlight by a photographer who had been given his name, but wasn't sure what his subject "did"—Adrian Smith and his blond wife, Eva, went up to the promenade deck, passed the melancholy ship's officer, and, finding a quiet aerie, put their elbows on the rail.

"We're going!" he cried presently, and they both laughed in ecstasy. "We've escaped. They can't get us now."

"Who?"

He waved his hand vaguely at the civic tiara.

"All those people out there. They'll come with their posses and their warrants and list of crimes we've committed, and ring the bell at our door on Park Avenue and ask for the Adrian Smiths, but what ho! the Adrian Smiths and their children and nurse are off for France."

"You make me think we really have committed crimes."

"They can't have you," he said, frowning. "That's one thing they're after me about—they know I haven't got any right to a person like you, and they're furious. That's one reason I'm glad to get away."

"Darling," said Eva.

She was 26—five years younger than he. She was something precious to everyone who knew her.

"I like this boat better than the *Majestic* or the *Aquitania*," she remarked, unfaithful to the ships that had served their honeymoon.

"It's much smaller."

"But it's very slick and it has all those little shops along the corridors. And I think the staterooms are bigger."

"The people are very formal—did you notice?—as if they thought everyone else was a card sharp. And in about four days half of them will be calling the other half by their first names."

Four of the people came by now—a quartet of young girls abreast, making a circuit of the deck. Their eight eyes swept momentarily toward Adrian and Eva, and then swept automatically back, save for one pair which lingered for an instant with a little start. They belonged to one of the girls in the middle, who was, indeed, the only passenger of the four. She was not more than 18—a dark little beauty with the fine crystal gloss over her that, in brunettes, takes the place of a blonde's bright glow.

"Now, who's that?" wondered Adrian. "I've seen her before."

"She's pretty," said Eva.

"Yes." He kept wondering, and Eva deferred mo-

*In 1929, when this story appeared in the* Post, *little girls wore anklesocks and patent Mary Janes; autos had fenders and running boards.*

mentarily to his distraction; then, smiling up at him, she drew him back into their privacy.

"Tell me more," she said.

"About what?"

"About us—what a good time we'll have, and how we'll be much better and happier, and very close always."

"How could we be any closer?" His arm pulled her to him.

"But I mean never even quarrel any more about silly things. You know, I made up my mind when you gave me my birthday present last week"—her fingers caressed the fine seed pearls at her throat—"that I'd try never to say a mean thing to you again."

"You never have, my precious."

Yet even as he strained her against his side she knew that the moment of utter isolation had passed almost before it had begun. His antennae were already out, feeling over this new world.

"Most of the people look rather awful," he said—"little and swarthy and ugly. Americans didn't used to look like that."

"They do look rather dreary," she agreed. "Let's

*"A dark little beauty with the fine crystal gloss over her that, in brunettes, takes the place of a blonde's bright glow." (1926)*

not get to know anybody, but just stay together."

A gong was beating now, and stewards were shouting down the decks, "Visitors ashore, please!" and voices rose to a strident chorus. For a while the gangplanks were thronged; then they were empty, and the jostling crowd behind the barrier waved and called unintelligible things, and kept up a grin of goodwill. As the stevedores began to work at the ropes a flat-faced, somewhat befuddled young man arrived in a great hurry and was assisted up the gangplank by a porter and a taxi driver. The ship having swallowed him as impassively as though he were a missionary for Beirut, a low, portentous vibration began. The pier with its faces commenced to slide by, and for a moment the boat was just a piece accidentally split off from it; then the faces became remote, voiceless, and the pier was one among many yellow blurs along the waterfront. Now the harbor flowed swiftly toward the sea.

On a northern parallel of latitude a hurricane was forming and moving south by southeast preceded by a strong west wind. On its course it was destined to swamp the *Peter I. Eudim* of Amsterdam, with a crew of 66, to break a boom on the largest boat in the world, and to bring grief and want to the wives of several hundred seamen. This liner, leaving New York Sunday evening, would enter the zone of the storm Tuesday, and of the hurricane late Wednesday night.

Tuesday afternoon Adrian and Eva paid their first visit to the smoking room. This was not in accord with their intentions—they had "never wanted to see a cocktail again" after leaving America—but they had forgotten the staccato loneliness of ships, and all activity centered about the bar. So they went in for just a minute.

It was full. There were those who had been there since luncheon, and those who would be there until dinner, not to mention a faithful few who had been there since nine this morning. It was a prosperous assembly, taking its recreation at bridge, solitaire, detective stories, alcohol, argument, and love. Up to this point you could have matched it in the club or casino life of any country, but over it all played a repressed nervous energy, a barely disguised impatience that extended to old and young alike. The cruise had begun, and they had enjoyed the beginning, but the show was not varied enough to last six days, and already they wanted it to be over.

At a table near them Adrian saw the pretty girl who had stared at him on the deck the first night. Again he was fascinated by her loveliness; there was no mist upon the brilliant gloss that gleamed through the

smoky confusion of the room. He and Eva had decided from the passenger list that she was probably "Miss Elizabeth D'Amido and maid," and he had heard her called Betsy as he walked past a deck-tennis game. Among the young people with her was the flat-nosed youth who had been "poured on board" the night of their departure; yesterday he had walked the deck morosely, but he was apparently reviving. Miss D'Amido whispered something to him, and he looked over at the Smiths with curious eyes. Adrian was new enough at being a celebrity to turn self-consciously away.

"There's a little roll. Do you feel it?" Eva demanded.

"Perhaps we'd better split a pint of champagne."

While he gave the order, a short colloquy was taking place at the other table; presently a young man rose and came over to them.

"Isn't this Mr. Adrian Smith?"

"Yes."

"We wondered if we couldn't put you down for the deck-tennis tournament. We're going to have a deck-tennis tournament."

"Why——" Adrian hesitated.

"My name's Stacomb," burst out the young man. "We all know your—your plays or whatever it is, and all that—and we wondered if you wouldn't like to come over to our table."

Somewhat overwhelmed, Adrian laughed; Mr. Stacomb, glib, soft, slouching, waited—evidently under the impression that he had delivered himself of a graceful compliment.

Adrian, understanding that, too, replied: "Thanks, but perhaps you'd better come over here."

"We've got a bigger table."

"But we're older and more—more settled."

The young man laughed kindly, as if to say, "That's all right."

"Put me down," said Adrian. "How much do I owe you?"

"One buck. Call me Stac."

"Why?" asked Adrian, startled.

"It's shorter."

When he had gone they smiled broadly.

"Heavens," Eva gasped, "I believe they are coming over."

They were. With a great draining of glasses, calling of waiters, shuffling of chairs, three boys and two girls moved to the Smiths' table. If there was any diffidence, it was confined to the hosts; for the new additions gathered around them eagerly, eyeing Adrian with respect—too much respect—as if to say: "This was probably a mistake and won't be amusing, but maybe we'll get something out of it to help us in our afterlife, like at school."

In a moment Miss D'Amido changed seats with one of the men and placed her radiant self at Adrian's side, looking at him with manifest admiration.

"I fell in love with you the minute I saw you," she said, audibly and without self-consciousness; "so I'll take all the blame for butting in. I've seen your play four times."

Adrian called a waiter to take their orders.

"You see," continued Miss D'Amido, "we're going into a storm, and you might be prostrated the rest of the trip, so I couldn't take any chances."

He saw that there was no undertone or innuendo in what she said, nor the need of any. The words themselves were enough, and the deference with which she neglected the young men and bent her politeness on him was somehow very touching. A little glow went over him; he was having rather more than a pleasant time.

Eva was less entertained; but the flat-nosed young man, whose name was Butterworth, knew people that she did, and that seemed to make the affair less careless and casual. She did not like meeting new people unless they had "something to contribute," and she was often bored by the great streams of them of all types and conditions, that passed through Adrian's life. She herself "had everything"—which is to say that she was well endowed with talents and with charm—and the mere novelty of people did not seem a sufficient reason for eternally offering everything up to them.

Half an hour later when she rose to go and see the children, she was content that the episode was over. It was colder on deck, with a damp that was almost rain, and there was a perceptible motion. Opening the door of her stateroom she was surprised to find the cabin steward sitting languidly on her bed, his head slumped upon the upright pillow. He looked at her listlessly as she came in, but made no move to get up.

"When you've finished your nap you can fetch me a new pillowcase," she said briskly.

Still the man didn't move. She perceived then that his face was green.

"You can't be seasick in here," she announced firmly. "You go and lie down in your own quarters."

"It's me side," he said faintly. He tried to rise, gave out a little rasping sound of pain, and sank back again. Eva rang for the stewardess.

A steady pitch, toss, roll had begun in earnest and she felt no sympathy for the steward, but only wanted to get him out as quick as possible. It was outrageous for a member of the crew to be seasick. When the stewardess came in Eva tried to explain this, but now her own head was whirring, and throwing herself on the bed, she covered her eyes.

"It's his fault." she groaned when the man was

*"We're going! We've escaped. They can't get at us now."*

*The* Europa, *built in Germany in 1929, was for a while the fastest liner afloat. She crossed the Atlantic in 4 days, 18 hours.*

assisted from the room. "I was all right and it made me sick to look at him. I wish he'd die."

In a few minutes Adrian came in.

"Oh, but I'm sick!" she cried.

"Why, you poor baby." He leaned over and took her in his arms. "Why didn't you tell me?"

"I was all right upstairs, but there was a steward—Oh, I'm too sick to talk."

"You'd better have dinner in bed."

"Dinner! Oh, my heavens!"

He waited solicitously, but she wanted to hear his voice, to have it drown out the complaining sound of the beams.

"Where've you been?"

"Helping to sign up people for the tournament."

"Will they have it if it's like this? Because if they do I'll just lose for you."

He didn't answer; opening her eyes, she saw that he was frowning.

"I didn't know you were going in the doubles," he said.

"Why, that's the only fun."

"I told the D'Amido girl I'd play with her."

"Oh."

"I didn't think. You know I'd much rather play with you."

"Why didn't you, then?" she asked coolly.

"It never occurred to me."

She remembered that on their honeymoon they had been in the finals and won a prize. Years passed. But Adrian never frowned in this regretful way unless he felt a little guilty. He stumbled about, getting his dinner clothes out of the trunk, and she shut her eyes.

When a particular violent lurch startled her awake again, he was dressed and tying his tie. He looked healthy and fresh, and his eyes were bright.

"Well, how about it?" he inquired. "Can you make it, or no?"

"No."

"Can I do anything for you before I go?"

"Where are you going?"

"Meeting those kids in the bar. Can I do anything for you?"

"No."

"Darling, I hate to leave you like this."

"Don't be silly. I just want to sleep."

That solicitous frown—when she knew he was crazy to be out and away from the close cabin. She was glad when the door closed. The thing to do was to sleep, sleep.

Up—down—sideways. Hey there, not so far! Pull her round the corner there! Now roll her, right—left——Crea-eak! Wrench! Swoop!

Some hours later Eva was dimly conscious of Adrian bending over her. She wanted him to put his arms around her and draw her up out of this dizzy lethargy, but by the time she was fully awake the cabin was empty. He had looked in and gone. When she awoke next the cabin was dark and he was in bed.

The morning was fresh and cool, and the sea was just enough calmer to make Eva think she could get up. They breakfasted in the cabin and with Adrian's help she accomplished an unsatisfactory makeshift toilet and they went up on the boat deck. The tennis tournament had already begun and was furnishing action for a dozen amateur movie cameras, but the majority of passengers were represented by lifeless bundles in deck chairs beside untasted trays.

Adrian and Miss D'Amido played their first match. She was deft and graceful, blatantly well. There was even more warmth behind her ivory skin than there had been the day before. The strolling first officer stopped and talked to her; half a dozen men whom she couldn't have known three days ago called her Betsy. She was already the pretty girl of the voyage.

But after a while Eva preferred to watch the gulls in the wireless masts and the slow slide of the roll-top sky. Most of the passengers looked silly with their movie cameras that they had all rushed to get and now didn't know what to use for, but the sailors painting the lifeboat stanchions were quiet and beaten and sympathetic, and probably wished, as she did, that the voyage was over.

Butterworth sat down on the deck beside her chair.

"They're operating on one of the stewards this morning. Must be terrible in this sea."

"Operating? What for?" she asked listlessly.

"Appendicitis. They have to operate now because we're going into worse weather. That's why they're having the ship's party tonight."

"Oh, the poor man!" she cried, realizing it must be her steward.

Adrian was showing off now by being very courteous and thoughtful in the game.

"Sorry. Did you hurt yourself? . . . No, it was my fault. . . . You better put on your coat right away, pardner, or you'll catch cold."

The match was over and they had won. Flushed and hearty, he came up to Eva's chair.

"How do you feel?"

"Terrible."

"Winners are buying a drink in the bar," he said apologetically.

"I'm coming, too," Eva said, but an immediate dizziness made her sink back in her chair.

"You'd better stay here. I'll send you up something."

She felt that his public manner had hardened toward her slightly.

"You'll come back?"

"Oh, right away."

She was alone on the boat deck, save for a solitary ship's officer who slanted obliquely as he paced the bridge. When the cocktail arrived she forced herself to drink it, and felt better. Trying to distract her mind with pleasant things, she reached back to the sanguine talks that she and Adrian had had before sailing: There was the little villa in Brittany, the children learning French—that was all she could think of now—the little villa in Brittany, the children learning French—so she repeated the words over and over to herself until they became as meaningless as the wide white sky. The why of their being here had suddenly eluded her; she felt unmotivated, accidental, and she wanted Adrian to come back quick, all responsive and tender, to reassure her. It was in the hope that there was some secret of graceful living, some real compensation for the lost, careless confidence of 21, that they were going to spend a year in France.

The day passed darkly, with fewer people around and a wet sky falling. Suddenly it was five o'clock, and they were all in the bar again, and Mr. Butterworth was telling her about his past. She took a good deal of champagne, but she was seasick dimly through it, as if the illness was her soul trying to struggle up through some thickening incrustation of abnormal life.

"You're my idea of a Greek goddess, physically," Butterworth was saying.

It was pleasant to be Mr. Butterworth's idea of a Greek goddess physically, but where was Adrian? He and Miss D'Amido had gone out on a forward deck to feel the spray. Eva heard herself promising to get out her colors and paint the Eiffel Tower on Butterworth's shirtfront for the party tonight.

When Adrian and Betsy D'Amido, soaked with spray, opened the door with difficulty against the driving wind and came into the now-covered security of the promenade deck, they stopped and turned toward each other.

"Well?" she said. But he only stood with his back to the rail, looking at her, afraid to speak. She was silent, too, because she wanted him to be first; so for a moment nothing happened. Then she made a step toward him, and he took her in his arms and kissed her forehead.

"You're just sorry for me, that's all." She began to cry a little. "You're just being kind."

"I feel terribly about it." His voice was taut and trembling.

"Then kiss me."

The deck was empty. He bent over her swiftly.

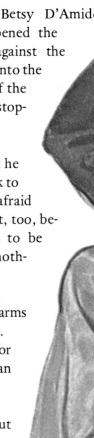

"No, I want you to really kiss me."

He could not remember when anything had felt so young and fresh as her lips. The rain lay, like tears shed for him, upon the softly shining porcelain cheeks. She was all beautifully new and immaculate, and her eyes were wild.

"I love you," she whispered. "I can't help loving you, can I? When I first saw you—oh, not on the boat, but over a year ago—Grace Heally took me to a rehearsal and suddenly you jumped up in the second row and began telling

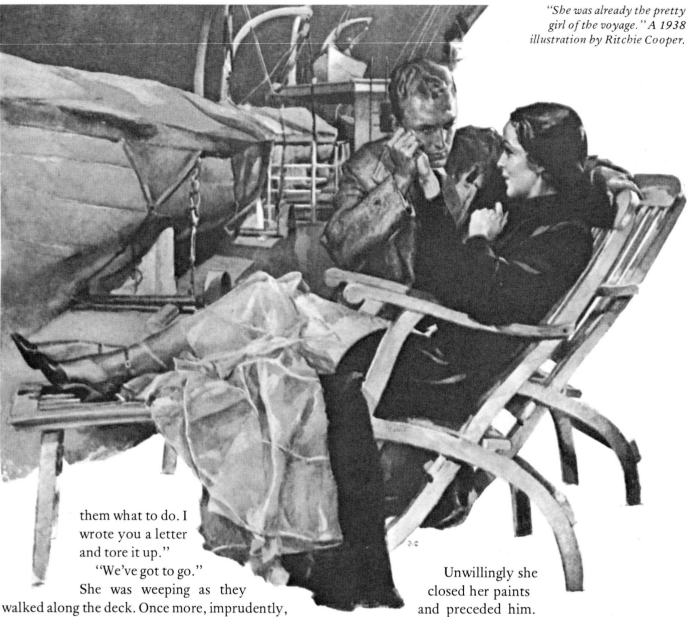

*"She was already the pretty girl of the voyage." A 1938 illustration by Ritchie Cooper.*

them what to do. I wrote you a letter and tore it up."

"We've got to go."

She was weeping as they walked along the deck. Once more, imprudently, she held up her face to him at the door of her cabin. His blood was beating through him in wild tumult as he walked on to the bar.

He was thankful that Eva scarcely seemed to notice him or to know that he had been gone. After a moment he pretended an interest in what she was doing.

"What's that?"

"She's painting the Eiffel Tower on my shirtfront for tonight," explained Butterworth.

"There," Eva laid away her brush and wiped her hands. "How's that?"

"A *chef-d'oeuvre.*"

Her eyes swept around the watching group, lingered casually upon Adrian.

"You're wet. Go and change."

"You come too."

"I want another champagne cocktail."

"You've had enough. It's time to dress for the party."

Unwillingly she closed her paints and preceded him.

"Stacomb's got a table for nine," he remarked as they walked along the corridor.

"The younger set," she said with unnecessary bitterness. "Oh, the younger set. And you just having the time of your life—with a child."

They had a long discussion in the cabin, unpleasant on her part and evasive on his, which ended when the ship gave a sudden gigantic heave, and Eva, the edge worn off her champagne, felt ill again. There was nothing to do but to have a cocktail in the cabin, and after that they decided to go to the party—she believed him now, or she didn't care.

Adrian was ready first—he never wore fancy dress.

"I'll go on up. Don't be long."

"Wait for me, please; it's rocking so."

He sat down on a bed, concealing his impatience.

"You don't mind waiting, do you? I don't want to parade up there all alone."

She was taking a tuck in an oriental costume rented from the ship's barber.

"Ships make people feel crazy," she said. "I think they're awful."

"Yes," he muttered absently.

"When it gets very bad I pretend I'm in the top of a tree, rocking to and fro. But finally I get pretending everything, and finally I have to pretend I'm sane when I know I'm not."

"If you get thinking that way you will go crazy."

"Look, Adrian." She held up the string of pearls before clasping them on. "Aren't they lovely?"

In Adrian's impatience she seemed to move around the cabin like a figure in a slow-motion picture. After a moment he demanded:

"Are you going to be long? It's stifling in here."

"You go on!" she fired up.

"I don't want——"

"Go on, please! You just make me nervous trying to hurry me."

With a show of reluctance he left her. After a moment's hesitation he went down a flight to a deck below and knocked at a door.

"Betsy."

"Just a minute."

She came out in the corridor attired in a red pea jacket and trousers borrowed from the elevator boy.

"Do elevator boys have fleas?" she demanded. "I've got everything in the world on under this as a precaution."

"I had to see you," he said quickly.

"Careful," she whispered. "Mrs. Worden, my chaperone, is across the way. She's sick."

"I'm sick for you."

They kissed suddenly, clung close together in the narrow corridor, swaying to and fro with the motion of the ship.

"Don't go away," she murmured.

"I've got to. I've——"

Her youth seemed to flow into him, bearing him up into a delicate romantic ecstasy that transcended passion. He couldn't relinquish it; he had discovered something that he had thought was lost with his own youth forever. As he walked along the passage he knew that he had stopped thinking, no longer dared to think.

He met Eva going into the bar.

"Where've you been?" she asked with a strained smile.

"To see about the table."

She was lovely; her cool distinction conquered the trite costume and filled him with a resurgence of approval and possessive pride. They sat down at a table.

The gale was rising hour by hour and the mere traversing of a passage had become a rough matter. In every stateroom trunks were lashed to the washstands and the *Vestris* disaster was being reviewed in detail by nervous ladies, tossing, ill and wretched, upon their beds. In the smoking room a stout gentleman had been hurled backward and suffered a badly cut head; and now the lighter chairs and tables were stacked and roped against the wall.

The crowd who had donned fancy dress and were dining together had swollen to about 16. The only remaining qualification for membership was the ability to reach the smoking room. They ranged from a Groton-Harvard lawyer to an ungrammatical broker they had nicknamed Gyp the Blood, but distinctions had disappeared; for the moment they were samurai, chosen from several hundred for their triumphant resistance to the storm.

The gala dinner, overhung sardonically with lanterns and streamers, was interrupted by great communal slides across the room, precipitate retirements, and spilled wine, while the ship roared and complained that under the panoply of a palace it was a ship after all. Upstairs afterward a dozen couples tried to dance, shuffling and galloping here and there in a crazy fandango, thrust around fantastically by a will alien to their own. In view of the condition of tortured hundreds below, there grew to be something indecent about it, like a revel in a house of mourning, and presently there was an egress of the ever-dwindling survivors toward the bar.

As the evening passed, Eva's feeling of unreality increased. Adrian had disappeared—presumably with Miss D'Amido—and her mind, distorted by illness and champagne, began to enlarge upon the fact; annoyance changed slowly to dark and brooding anger, grief to desperation. She had never tried to bind Adrian, never needed to—for they were serious people, with all sorts of mutual interests, and satisfied with each other—but this was a breach of the contract, this was cruel. How could he think that she didn't know?

It seemed several hours later that he leaned over her chair in the bar where she was giving some woman an impassioned lecture upon babies, and said:

"Eva, we'd better turn in."

Her lip curled. "So that you can leave me there and then come back to your 18-year——"

"Be quiet."

"I won't come to bed."

"Very well. Good night."

More time passed and the people at the table changed. The stewards wanted to close up the room, and thinking of Adrian—her Adrian—off somewhere saying tender things to someone fresh and lovely, Eva began to cry.

"But he's gone to bed," her last attendants assured her. "We saw him go."

She shook her head. She knew better. Adrian was lost. The long seven-year dream was broken. Probably she was punished for something she had done; as this thought occurred to her the shrieking timbers overhead began to mutter that she had guessed at last. This was for the selfishness to her mother, who hadn't wanted her to marry Adrian; for all the sins and omissions of her life. She stood up, saying she must go out and get some air.

The deck was dark and drenched with wind and rain. The ship pounded through valleys, fleeing from black mountains of water that roared toward it. Looking out at the night, Eva saw that there was no chance for them unless she could make atonement, propitiate the storm. It was Adrian's love that was demanded of her. Deliberately she unclasped her pearl necklace, lifted it to her lips—for she knew that with it went the freshest, fairest part of her life—and flung it out into the gale.

When Adrian awoke it was lunchtime, but he knew that some heavier sound than the bugle had called him up from his deep sleep. Then he realized that the trunk had broken loose from its lashings and was being thrown back and forth between a wardrobe and Eva's bed. With an exclamation he jumped up, but she was unharmed—still in costume and stretched out in deep sleep. When the steward had helped him secure the trunk, Eva opened a single eye.

"How are you?" he demanded, sitting on the side of the bed.

She closed the eye, opened it again.

"We're in a hurricane now," he told her. "The steward says it's the worst he's see in 20 years."

"My head," she muttered. "Hold my head."

"How?"

"In front. My eyes are going out. I think I'm dying."

"Nonsense. Do you want the doctor?"

She gave a funny little gasp that frightened him; he rang and sent the steward for the doctor.

The young doctor was pale and tired. There was stubble of beard upon his face. He bowed curtly as he came in and, turning to Adrian, said with scant ceremony.

"What's the matter?"

"My wife doesn't feel well."

"Well, then what is it that you want—a bromide?"

A little annoyed by his shortness, Adrian said: "You'd better examine her and see what she needs."

"She needs a bromide," said the doctor. "I've given orders that she is not to have any more to drink on this ship."

"Why not?" demanded Adrian in astonishment.

"Don't you know what happened last night?"

"Why, no, I was asleep."

"Mrs. Smith wandered around the boat for an hour, not knowing what she was doing. A sailor was set to follow her, and then the medical stewardess tried to get her to bed, and your wife insulted her."

"Oh, my heavens!" cried Eva faintly.

"The nurse and I had both been up all night with Steward Carton, who died this morning." He picked up his case. "I'll send down a bromide for Mrs. Smith. Good-bye."

For a few minutes there was silence in the cabin. Then Adrian put his arm around her quickly.

"Never mind," he said. "We'll straighten it out."

"I remember now." Her voice was an awed whisper. "My pearls. I threw them overboard."

"Threw them overboard!"

"Then I began looking for you."

"But I was here in bed."

"I didn't believe it; I thought you were with that girl."

"She collapsed during dinner. I was taking a nap down here."

Frowning, he rang the bell and asked the steward for luncheon and a bottle of beer.

"Sorry, but we can't serve any beer to your cabin, sir."

When he went out Adrian exploded: "This is an outrage. You were simply crazy from that storm and they can't be so high-handed. I'll see the captain."

"Isn't that awful?" Eva murmured. "The poor man died."

She turned over and began to sob into her pillow. There was a knock at the door.

"Can I come in?"

The assiduous Mr. Butterworth, surprisingly healthy and immaculate, came into the crazily tipping cabin.

"Well, how's the mystic?" he demanded of Eva. "Do you remember praying to the elements in the bar last night?"

"I don't want to remember anything about last night."

They told him about the stewardess, and with the telling the situation lightened; they all laughed.

*"Upstairs afterward a dozen couples tried to dance." A 1938 illustration by Ritchie Cooper.*

"I'm going to get you some beer to have with your luncheon," Butterworth said. "You ought to get up on deck."

"Don't go," Eva said. "You look so cheerful and nice."

"Just for 10 minutes."

When he had gone, Adrian rang for two baths.

"The thing is to put on our best clothes and walk proudly three times around the deck," he said.

"Yes." After a moment she added abstractedly: "I like that young man. He was awfully nice to me last night when you'd disappeared."

The bath steward appeared with the information that bathing was too dangerous today. They were in the midst of the wildest hurricane on the North Atlantic in 10 years; there were two broken arms this morning from attempts to take baths. An elderly lady had been thrown down a staircase and was not expected to live. Furthermore, they had received the SOS signal from several boats this morning.

"Will we go to help them?"

"They're all behind us, sir, so we have to leave them to the *Mauretania*. If we tried to turn in this sea the portholes would be smashed."

This array of calamities minimized their own troubles. Having eaten a sort of luncheon and drunk the beer provided by Butterworth, they dressed and went on deck.

Despite the fact that it was only possible to progress step by step, holding on to rope or rail, more people were abroad than on the day before. Fear had driven them from their cabins, where the trunks bumped and the waves pounded the portholes, and they awaited momentarily the call to the boats. Indeed, as Adrian and Eva stood on the transverse deck above the second class, there was a bugle call, followed by a gathering of stewards and stewardesses on the deck below. But the boat was sound; it had outlasted one of its cargo—Steward James Carton was being buried at sea.

It was very British and sad. There were the rows of stiff, disciplined men and women standing in the driving rain, and there was a shape covered by the flag of the Empire that lived by the sea. The chief purser read the service, a hymn was sung, the body slid off into the hurricane. With Eva's burst of wild weeping for this humble end, some last string snapped within her. Now she really didn't care. She responded eagerly when Butterworth suggested that he get some champagne to their cabin. Her mood worried Adrian; she wasn't used to so much drinking and he wondered what he ought to do. At his suggestion that they sleep instead, she merely laughed, and the bromide the doctor had sent stood untouched on the washstand. Pretending to listen to the insipidities of several Mr. Stacombs, he watched her; to his surprise and discomfort she seemed on intimate and even sentimental terms with Butterworth, and he wondered if this was a form of revenge for his attention to Betsy D'Amido.

The cabin was full of smoke; the voices went on incessantly; the suspension of activity, the waiting for the storm's end, was getting on his nerves. They had been at sea only four days; it was like a year.

The two Mr. Stacombs left finally, but Butterworth remained. Eva was urging him to go for another bottle of champagne.

"We've had enough," objected Adrian. "We ought to go to bed."

"I won't go to bed!" she burst out. "You must be crazy! You think you can play around all you want, and then, when I find somebody I—I like, you want to put me to bed."

"You're hysterical."

"On the contrary, I've never been so sane."

"I think you'd better leave us, Butterworth," Adrian said. "Eva doesn't know what she's saying."

"He won't go. I won't let him go." She clasped Butterworth's hand passionately. "He's the only person that's been half decent to me."

"You'd better go, Butterworth," repeated Adrian.

The young man looked at him uncertainly.

"It seems to me you're being unjust to your wife," he ventured.

"My wife isn't herself."

"That's no reason for bullying her."

Adrian lost his temper. "You get out of here!" he cried.

The two men looked at each other for a moment in silence. Then Butterworth turned to Eva, said, "I'll be back later," and left the cabin.

"Eva, you've got to pull yourself together," said Adrian when the door closed.

She didn't answer, looked at him from sullen, half-closed eyes.

"I'll order dinner here for us both and then we'll try to get some sleep."

"I want to go up and send a wireless."

"Who to?"

"Some Paris lawyer. I want a divorce."

In spite of his annoyance, he laughed. "Don't be silly."

"Then I want to see the children."

"Well, go and see them. I'll order dinner."

*"The ship pounded through valleys, fleeing from dark mountains of water that roared toward it." By A. O. Fischer.*

He waited for her in the cabin 20 minutes. Then impatiently he opened the door across the corridor; the nurse told him that Mrs. Smith had not been there.

With a sudden prescience of disaster he ran upstairs, glanced in the bar, the salons, even knocked at Butterworth's door. Then a quick round of the decks, feeling his way through the black spray and rain. A sailor stopped him at a network of ropes.

"Orders are no one goes by, sir. A wave has gone over the wireless room."

"Have you seen a lady?"

"There was a young lady here——" He stopped and glanced around. "Hello, she's gone."

"She went up the stairs!" Adrian said anxiously. "Up to the wireless room!"

The sailor ran up to the boat deck; stumbling and slipping, Adrian followed. As he cleared the protected sides of the companionway, a tremendous body struck the boat a staggering blow and, as she keeled over to an angle of 45 degrees, he was thrown in a helpless roll down the drenched deck, to bring up dizzy and bruised against a stanchion.

"Eva!" he called. His voice was soundless in the black storm. Against the faint light of the wireless room window he saw the sailor making his way forward.

"Eva!"

The wind blew him like a sail up against a lifeboat. Then there was another shuddering crash, and high over his head, over the very boat, he saw a gigantic, glittering white wave, and in the split second that it balanced there he became conscious of Eva, standing beside a ventilator 20 feet away. Pushing out from the stanchion, he lunged desperately toward her, just as the wave broke with a smashing roar. For a moment the rushing water was five feet deep, sweeping with enormous force toward the side, and then a human body was washed against him, and frantically he clutched it and was swept with it back toward the rail. He felt his body bump against it, but desperately he held on to his burden; then, as the ship rocked slowly back, the two of them, still joined by his fierce grip, were rolled out exhausted on the wet planks. For a moment he knew no more.

Two days later, as the boat train moved tranquilly south toward Paris, Adrian tried to persuade his children to look out the window at the Norman countryside.

"It's beautiful," he assured them. "All the little farms like toys.

"I like the boat better," said Estelle.

Her parents exchanged an infanticidal glance.

"The boat is still rocking for me," Eva said with a shiver. "Is it for you?"

"No. Somehow, it all seems a long way off. Even the passengers looked unfamiliar going through the customs."

He hesitated. "By the way, I cashed Butterworth's check for him."

"You're a fool. You'll never see the money again."

"He must have needed it pretty badly or he would not have come to me."

A pale and wan girl, passing along the corridor, recognized them and put her head through the door.

"How do you feel?"

"Awful."

"Me, too," agreed Miss D'Amido. "I'm vainly hoping my fiance will recognize me at the Gare du Nord. Do you know two waves went over the wireless room?"

"So we heard," Adrian answered dryly.

She passed gracefully along the corridor and out of their life.

"The real truth is that none of it happened," said Adrian after a moment. "It was a nightmare—an incredibly awful nightmare."

"Then, where are my pearls?"

"Darling, there are better pearls in Paris. I'll take the responsibility for those pearls. My real belief is that you saved the boat."

"Adrian, let's never get to know anyone else, but just stay together always—just we two."

He tucked her arm under his and they sat close. "Who do you suppose those Adrian Smiths on the boat were?" he demanded. "It certainly wasn't me."

"Nor me."

"It was two other people," he said, nodding to himself. "There are so many Smiths in this world."

DRAWN BY EMLEN MCCONNELL

*The good life afloat. The lady swimmer (left) and her friends listen to music from an early Edison phonograph.*

# Luxury at Sea in 1904

## BY RENE BACHE

If his steam yacht costs the rich man a great deal of money, it is undeniably the most luxurious and delightful toy imaginable. It is practically a Fifth Avenue mansion afloat, reduced in scale and more compact, but with the same conveniences and equally

sumptuous accommodations. The dining room is superb, with elaborate decorations and furniture of rare woods beautifully carved; the library, which is a lounging place, with leather-covered chairs and sofas and plenty of books, runs clear across the boat, and has a dome skylight of cathedral glass. There is at least one bathroom, tiled and with a porcelain tub, for each two staterooms, and to the tubs are supplied both fresh and salt water, hot and cold. The pantry is a roomy apartment, with dumbwaiter and cold-storage box, and an ice machine of one-ton capacity is operated by a dynamo. Nearly all of the machinery is electrical, save that used for the propulsion of the craft; there are powerful electric searchlights, and four or five hundred incandescent lights are distributed through the vessel.

The cost of running a steam yacht necessarily varies with its size. A 60-footer may be kept in commission for $300 a month, not counting food supplies. For a 150-footer the monthly expense would be $3,000 perhaps. But when it comes to a pleasure craft like Pierpont Morgan's *Corsair*, 304 feet on the waterline, or John Jacob Astor's *Nourmahal*, which is even bigger, the outlay is enormously greater. It costs about $20,000 a month to run the *Corsair*, and it is probable that Mr. Astor's bills for the *Nourmahal* in the summertime amount to not less than $25,000 every 30 days. The payroll of the officers and crew of such a vessel, which is a good-sized steamship, will touch $4,500 or possibly $5,000 a month.

A first-class steam yacht carries a crew of 50 or more.

Such a boat consumes 20 tons of coal a day, and at that rate, if she is kept going five months in the year, she will burn up something like 3,000 tons, the item of fuel alone coming to $10,000 for the season. For the rest of the year she is laid up in a basin, at an expense of $200 a month, and the cleaning and painting she has to undergo cost a pretty penny. It takes two weeks and an expenditure of $1,000 to lay her up, and a couple of months and $5,000 to put her in commission again. From these figures it is easy to understand where the money goes for a steam yacht, though it should be realized that bills for food supplies (not reckoned in the above account) are simply huge, especially when much entertaining is done. Anybody would be interested to know what it cost Cornelius Vanderbilt, on his recent trip abroad, to entertain Emperor William on board his yacht, and to meet on an appropriately sumptuous scale certain other social obligations which were imposed upon him by his intimacy with the great ones of

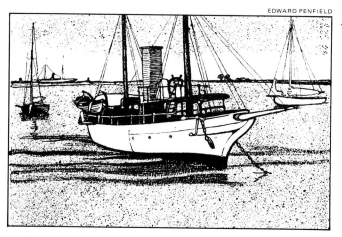

EDWARD PENFIELD

*A 1903 illustration shows well-dressed children playing pirate aboard the family yacht.*

the earth. Very possibly he did not get off for less than $100,000 for a few weeks' amusement.

But what is the use of being a multimillionaire unless you can enjoy yourself without making sordid comparisons between your bankbook and your check stubs? When the late Pierre Lorillard, not long before his death, ordered a boat to be built for him, he ransacked Europe for her furnishings. Even the chandeliers were imported, because there was nothing of the kind beautiful enough in this country. Unfortunately, he died before the yacht was finished; the things he had purchased were never put into her, and the hull was sold to some other rich man at a bargain.

Not a few rich men nowadays prefer sailing yachts, because of the superior accommodations which they afford. There is more comfort to be had, they assert, in a 100-foot schooner than in a 200-foot steam yacht. Such a schooner costs only about $30,000, and has a crew of 25, with 18 before the mast. Whereas a steam yacht is largely occupied by machinery and coal, which take up nearly the whole of the middle portion of the vessel, in a schooner the entire body of the craft is available for living purposes. Even a sloop, 60 or 70 feet long, and costing $18,000, perhaps, will carry six or eight cabin passengers very cozily.

When the multimillionaire takes a holiday jaunt to Europe he commonly pays $2,500 or $3,000 for his booking on a transatlantic liner, securing at this price accommodations for himself, wife, and two children, perhaps, with a couple of servants, the latter being rated as first-class passengers. The rooms assigned to him—three to five in number, connected, and as gorgeous as restricted space permits—are in a part of the vessel where the motion is least. Of course, he gives huge fees (the stewardess will expect at least $25), but the comfort enjoyed will be greatly augmented thereby. To common mortals there would seem to be nothing possible beyond, in the way of luxurious voyaging; but for the occasional and uncommon person, who is nearly always an American with unlimited cash, there is usually an "imperial suite" (such as that in which the Cornelius Vanderbilts returned to New York recently), which can be hired at $5,000 for the seven-day trip.

*The age of sail lingered among the wealthy and their yachts provided jobs for some of the seamen displaced by the shift to steam.*

*People called it "the only way to travel"—first class on the* Queen *with one's car (this is a 1930 Lincoln) stowed in the hold.*

# Farewell to the Queen Mary

## BY ANNE CHAMBERLIN

When the lists were finally drawn for the final Atlantic crossing in 1967, we were 1,398 adults, 45 children, 1 immigration officer, 4 bankers, 1 shop manager, 4 Distressed British Seamen, 1 stowaway, 1,013 crew, 1 dog, and 1 parakeet, bound for Southampton. Our procession down the Hudson was a festival—sparkling jets of water from the fireboats, swooping helicopters, launches, sea gulls, crowds along the shore, a man singing "Auld Lang Syne" through a bullhorn, 15 people who forgot to get off and had to go back with the pilot—everything just as it ought to be.

But as the passengers began to sort themselves out, you could see that the long hot summer on the waiting list had taken its toll. Dozens of people accustomed to traveling first class had to settle for cabin, or even tourist—an obscure territory located somewhere near the propeller shafts. The stowaway told me, after he had paid his passage and been promoted to a tourist-class cabin, that he'd had more room in the ship's jail.

To make life bearable for the exiles, they had unlocked the doors between the classes, which blurred the carefully layered distinctions that were a vital part of the original architecture. You could no longer pinpoint members of the Establishment by their cabin numbers.

Even a first-class ticket didn't guarantee one of the *Queen Mary*'s fabled luxury suites, paneled in zebrano, patashte, and thuja wood, with ruffled printed sateen bedspreads on the beds. One of my shipmates drew a cabin he called the Iron Lung. It must have been like mine—a sort of L-shaped tunnel, ending in a washbasin, with a fan to stir the trapped air and an electric clock with trembling hands that wrenched themselves from minute to minute with a loud clunk. It told the hour, ship's time, but not whether it was night or day. Which soon didn't matter anyway.

And it took more than a ticket to prove you were first-class material. The impeccable room stewards—who spend a long apprenticeship in the other classes before reaching the refinement of first—have five and a half days to straighten you out so you're fit to enter England, but it isn't always easy for them. ("We've always had the same good class of passengers in the suite rooms," one of them reassured me. "Handed down from generation to generation. But don't quote me.")

The *Queen Mary* wasn't built to be a floating resort for dallying around the tropics with a load of lotus eaters. It was built, like England itself, to stay steadfastly on course in a ghastly climate. Like putting to sea in the Royal Albert Hall.

The first-class public rooms, whose carvings, paintings, murals, lighting fixtures, furnishings, and mirrors

*Well-dressed passengers, by McClelland Barclay. (1929)*

were considered the wonder of their time, are of a school of English splendor that runs to pale browns, 40-watt bulbs, and papier-mâché coal under veined-marble mantels. In the great Promenade Deck Lounge the overstuffed chairs, deep rugs, tall brown columns reaching three decks above your head give you the feeling you've sunk forever into a bottomless amber sea. It is used for Selections at the Organ in the morning, Light Orchestral Concert and tea in the afternoon, Episcopal Divine Service on Sunday (with the surrounding bars reverently closed). At night it is the setting for bingo, "horse racing," and general revelry, featuring the ship's Cabaret Artistes.

The hallway outside is a rarefied shopping center—French perfumes, English commemorative crystal and china, Swiss watches. Parked between the shops was a blue-green Rover 2000 TC sedan, which could be ordered through the purser.

There was a corner for everyone in all this vastness and no danger of having to speak to strangers. Some passengers spent five days in the writing room, turning out fathomless acres of *Queen Mary* postcards. Some bundled in steamer rugs and snoozed in their deck chairs. The boat deck was divided among the grim pacers in mufflers and yachting caps, the arm-in-arm strollers who looked as though they might have come up from tourist, and a man from Connecticut who ran a mile in sweat pants every morning before breakfast.

As the aimless hours slid by, lunch and dinner became the main events of the day. Lunch was what you did whatever you did in the morning to work up an appetite for. Dinner was what you spent the afternoon (after tea and a nap, that is) getting dressed for.

It is terribly important, in the first-class dining room, where you sit. The head waiter and his assistant spent most of the voyage crouched over a passenger list and table charts with pencils and lots of erasers, trying to harmonize people's sense of importance with the available prestigious seats. Some of the pressure came off the captain's table because a lot of our most celebrated passengers elected to take their meals in the Verandah Grill, a sort of extra-price eating club with a sophisticated black rug, romantic lamps on the tables, a view of the back porch, and special kitchens that can produce, a knowing friend assured me, pheasant with the shot left in.

People are apparently only signed up for the Verandah Grill as they are for Eton—from birth. Before we had backed out onto the Hudson, there was a waiting list of 90 for every meal but breakfast, which isn't served there. Long after dinner there was dancing until dawn for anyone who could squeeze in the door, and the band played things like "Yes, We Have No Bananas."

The fare in first class was what the English call Continental and the French call English and which is an enduring testimony to an indestructible race. There were the tweedy things like Braised Chump Chop, Leicester Brawn, and Haunch of Venison, and then a whole category of dishes beyond the *ice cream* and *sherbet* called *savouries*, which even the waiter sometimes couldn't explain. When I asked him what Croute Ritchie was, he said, "Did I say creamed haddock last night?"

At the entrance to the dining room was a three-foot-high bust of the founder of the line, carved in margarine (Beethoven in butter, one of my tablemates kept calling it), which was surrounded by pink cakes with "God Speed Elizabeth II" inscribed on the icing. It was one more reminder that we were saluting a vanishing way of life. If the founder held up rather better than some of the passengers, it may have been because he was taken away every evening promptly after dinner to a refrigerator, while the rest of us faced a night of merrymaking, urged by the captain to "get on with the dancing and the gaiety."

There was a whole school of sentimentalists who felt they had to steal things. The menus vanished so fast at every meal that the waiters had to beg to have one returned so we could order dessert. If you put down a fork between bites, the waiter would whisk it away to lock it up so that it would still be around for the next meal. At my table the silver cream pitcher and sugar bowl had long since gone, along with the ashtrays. The captain's rose bowl, a splendid affair in carved silver which had been at his table since the ship was put in service, had disappeared the last time the ship landed at Southampton. Someone made off with a mirror and a glass-framed deck plan the first night out. A seagoing gentleman at my table noticed that the builder's plaque, affixed under the bridge when the ship was launched, was losing screws at the rate of one a night. You had to fight for clothes hangers. I learned at lifeboat drill, when I was the only passenger without one, that an earlier occupant of my cell had made off with its life jacket.

The captain hardly had time to drive, there were so many messages to read and reply to. Telegrams from the ladies who had sat at his table through the years, or perhaps some other table that they thought was his. "My son-in-law has told me you are sailing for the last time. . . .You might not remember me after 21 years." ("I'm afraid I don't actually.") "Kind thoughts and a little nostalgia" . . . "Farewell" . . . "My congratulations. . . ." ("I regret I can't remember *her*, either.") "I don't know what it means," the captain said, holding up one cable. "But I replied to it anyway."

In between, he exhorted us to dress well ("we must uphold the first-class side of the ship; she is nearing the end of her span of life, but in beautiful condition still"). And every evening he urged us to greater heights of gaiety. "Let's go out with a bang," he kept saying to groups of passengers. "Up with the flag and down with the drink." We did what we could.

I suppose our creative peak was reached at the Monday Night Fancy Headdress Contest. The captain said they were the finest headdresses he'd seen since he took command of the ship. "They are all so jolly good I am grateful to you all."

Veteran passengers showed their mettle with complicated structures—a whole racetrack, for one, mounted on headbands.

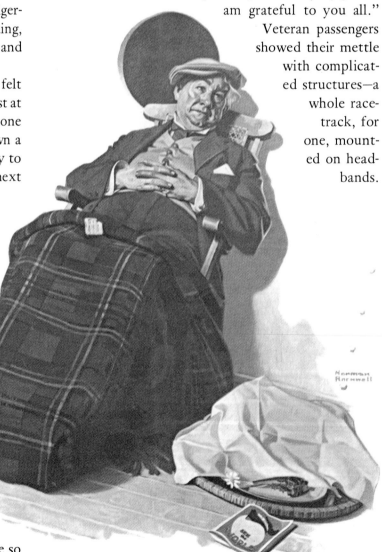

*A comfortable passenger, by Norman Rockwell. (1923)*

*A 1960* Post *cover by James Williamson features the shipboard romance—an ocean voyage without one was incomplete.*

My own favorites were a creation called "Trees"—two metal shoe trees flopping at the wearer's ears—and "The Ship Rolls"—four buns and two soggy croissants tied around like a garland.

Finally we came to the Ultimate Night, our last at sea, when the captain gave yet another farewell speech, urging us to still greater paroxysms of gaiety, his tears glistening in the lights ("I am a Welshman and very sentimental"). Balloons were loosed from the ceiling. We danced wildly for some of the prizes of champagne lined up by the dance band, and then shamelessly stole the rest. Felipe and Olga, the Cabaret Artistes, came out with a Chianti bottle and frantically tossed each other about the dance floor. He ate part of her skirt. She dropped an earring. They shouted. He chewed her ear. The rest of her dress came off, and he charged offstage with her as if her stiffened body were a javelin. We all milled out on the dance floor, knee deep in the paper streamers, while the band played "Britannia Rules the Waves."

They should have pulled the plug then, of course, and sunk us all, fixed there in our finest hour.

# They Are All Gone

## BY WALTER LORD

It's hard to believe they are gone. The piers are still there. The bon-boyage baskets, piled high with impractical fruits and jellies, still line the shelves of the gourmet shops. In midtown Manhattan there's even a postcard still for sale, showing the *Queen Elizabeth,* the *Mauretania,* a *Sylvania*-class Cunarder, the *America*, and the *Independence* at their berths, as though they were sailing tomorrow.

But there is no one of these fine liners—and nearly all too—have vanished tomorrow. Every transatlantic the others from service. They are gone as completely as the dirigible, and almost as fast. If the riverboats quietly faded away like a genteel lady in polite decline—if the railroads sagged into shameless decay like a Bowery bum—the Atlantic liner was taken from us like a good friend hit by a truck: swiftly, mercilessly, and leaving a sudden emptiness that is only beginning to be felt.

Perhaps it's better that way. At least the ocean traveler has been spared the pain of a slow decline. He will never feel the pang of the train buff, who must suffer through that long twilight of boarded-up stations, leaky plumbing, broken seats, peeling paint, and lavatories awash with dirty towels and crumpled cups.

On the Atlantic liner the stewards' jackets were starched to the end, and all the memories are pleasant: the creaking woodwork . . . the noon whistle . . . the morning bouillon . . . the hum of the rigging . . . the clack of shuffleboard disks on the boat deck.

*In 1932 A. O. Fischer painted a liner looking like a ghost ship. By 1970 the liners were ghosts; jet planes had replaced them.*

# Sea Lore
# and Legends

DRAWN BY
WALTER H. EVERETT

# Sailors Take Warning

*In olden times, tragedy was a commonplace of life at sea.*

She is a ghost ship, doomed to sail forever some limbo sea between Heaven and Hell because her captain's sins are unforgiven. Any sailor who sights her will die, and a ship whose path she crosses will never reach port. She is the *Flying Dutchman*, immortalized in an opera by Richard Wagner, or, to French sailors, *La Belle Rosalie*.

There are bad-luck birds as well as bad-luck phantom ships at sea, according to tradition. "The Rime of the Ancient Mariner" by Samuel Taylor Coleridge tells how harm will come to anyone who kills an albatross.

The men who went to sea in sailing ships were not more ignorant and gullible than others in their time, but they did live very close to death and disaster. The sea was wide and empty and mysterious before the invention of radio and weather forecasting. It is not surprising that the sailor turned to good-luck charms as a kind of insurance, and that he saw omens and portents in anything unusual.

The sailor was on guard even before he went on board his ship. He considered it bad luck to meet a priest or a spinster on his way to the dock. He especially feared meeting someone with crossed eyes or a squint, as such a person could cast the Evil Eye on him and jinx the voyage. He was careful to step onto the ship with his right foot, as using his left would bring bad luck. When it came time to sail he worried lest someone, even a well-wisher, should point at the ship or stand watching until the ship was out of sight, as that could bring bad luck. In some places friends of the sailors threw old shoes after the ship to bring her good luck, in the same way they would throw shoes after a newly married couple.

To prevent death by drowning, sailors wore gold earrings. Even more effective was carrying a caul—the membrane that sometimes covers the face of a human infant at birth—and it was not unusual for sailors to advertise in newspapers for cauls, offering sums as high as $60 for them. Sailors would not say the word "drowning" for fear of tempting fate. Some sailors would hesitate before saving another man from drowning, believing that the sea became the lifelong enemy of the rescuer who snatched away her prey.

Another charm that was supposed to give protection from drowning was the feather of a wren—especially if the wren was killed on New Year's Day. This belief came from an old legend about a beautiful mermaid who sang sweetly to sailors and lured them to their deaths. A brave knight who tried to kill her, to save the lives of seamen, was foiled when she turned herself into a wren. This belief led, unfortunately, to the slaughter of many innocent birds each New Year's Day. In Ireland, children went from door to door begging for "a

*Howard Pyle used the family gardener/handyman as model when he painted the doomed captain of the stormswept* Flying Dutchman.

penny to bury the wren,'' then spent the money on candy.

The beautiful woman, nymph, or mermaid who lures seamen to their deaths appears often in old legends. In Homer's *Odyssey* there are the sirens who perch on dangerous rocks, singing so sweetly that no man can resist approaching them. Odysseus passes by in safety only because he has plugged his men's ears with wax and had them bind him securely to the mast of his ship.

It is not surprising that men who lived on ships for months at a time dreamed of beautiful women and

*Shipwreck was the fate mariners feared most. Those who survived voyaged on in open boats or clung to rafts improvised from wreckage. In warm seas, sharks were their patient escorts. Painting by A. O. Fischer.*

Speaking to the wind in a coaxing way was a safe way of calling it to a becalmed ship. One might also scratch the mast with the fingernails, or burn an old broom.

A sailor would not sew or mend during a storm, for fear of "sewing on" the bad weather and prolonging it.

It was sometimes said that a storm would subside if a naked woman appeared before it. For this reason figureheads were sometimes women with bared breasts. For less daring shipowners there were figurehead ladies with low-necked dresses or very short skirts.

St. Elmo's fire, the harmless halo of lightning that sometimes appeared at the masthead, was a good omen that meant the worst of a storm was over. (Today, jet plane passengers are sometimes startled to see this eerie bluish light flickering on wingtips.)

To predict the weather, sailors recited this verse: "Red sky at night, sailor's delight; red sky in the morning, sailors take warning!"

Pets carried aboard ship generally brought bad luck, though on British ships a cat was thought to bring good luck.

Sailors usually considered woman passengers unlucky, since both sea and ship were female and might be jealous.

Carrying a corpse aboard ship was always regarded as unlucky; this is one reason why people who died at sea were generally buried at sea. If the body had to be transported it was placed in a coffin set at right angles to the ship's keel, and when port was reached the coffin was unloaded before the living passengers were allowed to disembark.

To prevent shipwrecks, sailors would nail a horseshoe or a silver coin to a ship's mast. They would never leave a hatch cover upside-down, as this was a sure sign the ship itself would turn over.

Ships were themselves considered lucky or unlucky. Laying the keel on a Friday or launching the ship on a Friday was sure to bring bad luck, and it was bad luck to rename a ship after it had been christened.

Most customs having to do with launching ships date from ancient times when ships were regarded as carrying the souls of goddesses (this is why a ship is "she" rather than "he"). To appease the goddess and bring good luck, enemy captives or slaves were sacrificed and their blood was splashed on the ship's keel. Later blood-red wine was substituted—and today we use a bottle of champagne.

came to half-believe that they might exist in the sea.

Many nautical superstitions have to do with weather, as it was a life-or-death factor in the lives of men at sea. The sailor did not whistle on board ship, for fear of whistling up a storm. In a dead calm, however, he might try whistling softly in hopes of producing a breeze.

# Sea Sayings—A Nautical Glossary

**Abaft**. Opposite of before. Farther toward the stern of the ship than some other object.

**Aboveboard**. Above the deck. Because anything aboveboard was visible, the term came to mean open or fair dealing.

**Aft**. Toward the stern of the ship. It can be an expression of position or of motion.

**Aweigh**. The anchor is aweigh at the moment it is no longer secured in the ground.

**Banyan Days**. Days on which no meat was served in the English navy. The name came from the Hindu merchants, who would not eat meat. The custom was introduced by

*"Sculling" is a variant of competitive rowing in which each oarsman (oarsperson?) controls two oars.*

Queen Elizabeth I to economize on the cost of supplying the ships.

**Bells, or Ship's Bells**. The system of marking time aboard ship. The six watches are divided into four hours each, and the passing of time during the watch is marked by strokes on the bell every half hour. One bell marks the end of the first half hour, two bells the end of the second, with eight bells marking the end of each watch.

**Booty**. The goods which, when a ship was captured at sea, were distributed among the captors at once. Originally it meant everything that could be picked up by hand above the deck.

**Cuddy**. A cabin in the stern of the ship for the captain and his passengers.

**Doldrums**. The calm area which lies inside the trade winds of either hemisphere. It also came to mean the depression the crews suffered while their ships lay motionless in these areas.

**Forecastle** (pronounced fo'c'sle). The living space of the crew in the front of the ship, below the forecastle deck. In the oldest fighting ships archers were stationed here to attack enemy vessels.

**Galley Pepper**. The soot and ashes which occasionally fell into food while it was being cooked.

**Galligaskins**. The seamen's wide breeches worn on the old sailing warships. Because they were made out of canvas, they were good protection against wet weather.

**Jack Tar**. Slang for a British seaman. Tar is shortened from tarpaulin.

**Jetsam**. Goods deliberately thrown overboard from a ship at sea, for instance to lighten her if she is in danger. Flotsam refers to goods accidentally lost overboard.

**Lee**. The side of a ship away from the wind.

**Limey**. Slang for a British seaman. All British ships were required to carry a stock of lime juice on board as a precaution against scurvy.

**Mizzen**. The last mast of a three-masted schooner or the third mast of a square-rigged sailing ship.

**Oakum**. Tarred fibers from old ropes, used for caulking the seams of wooden ships. The unraveling of rope into oakum was an old naval punishment. It was tedious work and very hard on the hands.

**Poop Deck**. The short deck at the stern of a ship, raised above the quarterdeck. It formed the roof of the round house or cuddy.

**Port**. The left side of a vessel looking toward the front. The name comes from the old merchant ships, which had a loading port on the left side. An aid to remembering: "left" and "port" have the same number of letters.

**Quarterdeck**. The part of the upper deck abaft the

mainmast. Customarily only officers use the quarter-deck, since it is the part of the ship from which the captain commands.

**Salt Horse**. Slang for the salted beef used as victuals before refrigeration. The beef was very tough as it came out of the cask, hence the expression.

**Scrimshaw**. The art of carving on the teeth of whales or the tusks of walrus, developed by American whalemen. The name derives from an Admiral Scrimshaw.

**Scuppers**. Holes cut in the ship's bulwarks to let water on deck drain away down the side of the ship.

**Shanty** or **Chantey**. Songs sung on board ship to lighten the labor of the sailors. All follow the same pattern of short verses and rollicking choruses.

**Starboard**. The right side of a ship, looking toward the front. It comes from steer-board, the oar which, before the invention of the hanging rudder, projected from the starboard side of the ship.

**Wet**. Slang meaning stupid.

*"Sloop" is a fore-and-aft rigged boat with just one mast stepped well forward. Painting by Anton Otto Fischer.*

# Under the Black Flag

## BY HOWARD PYLE

*One would hardly expect a sober Quaker gentleman to ride such a hobby, but Howard Pyle acquired over his lifetime an abiding interest in pirates. A careful researcher and historian, he probably knew more about the "outcast of the sea" than any other writer of his time.*

*"It is not because of his life of adventure and daring that I admire this one of my favorite heroes," he wrote. "He was a man who knew his own mind and what he wanted."*

*It is as an artist and teacher who established a tradition of action-filled, colorful illustration that Howard Pyle is best known. Of the artists whose work appears in this book, Anton Otto Fischer, N. C. Wyeth, Sarah S. Stilwell Weber, Henry J. Soulen, and Harvey T. Dunn were all his students.*

Why is it that a little spice of deviltry lends not an unpleasantly titillating twang to the great mass of respectable flour that goes to make up the pudding of our modern civilization? And pertinent to this question another—Why is it that the pirate has, and always has had, a certain lurid glamour of the heroical enveloping him round about? Is there, deep under the accumulated debris of culture, a hidden groundwork of the old-time savage? Is there even in these well-regulated times an unsubdued nature in the respectable mental household of every one of us that still kicks against the pricks of law and order? To make my meaning more clear, would not every boy, for instance—that is, every boy of any account—rather be a pirate captain than a Member of Parliament? And we ourselves—would we not rather read such a story as that of Captain Avery's capture of the East Indian treasure ship, with its beautiful princess and load of jewels

(which gems he sold by the handful, history sayeth, to a Bristol merchant), than, say, one of Bishop Atterbury's sermons, or the goodly Master Robert Boyle's religious romance of "Theodora and Didymus"? It is to be apprehended that to the unregenerate nature of most of us there can be but one answer to such a query.

In the pleasurable warmth the heart feels in answer to tales of derring-do, Nelson's battles are all mightily interesting; but, even in spite of their romance of splendid courage, I fancy that the majority of us would rather turn back over the leaves of history to read how Drake captured the Spanish treasure ship in the South Sea, and of how he divided such a quantity of booty in the Island of Plate (so named because of the tremendous dividend there declared) that it had to be measured in quart bowls, being too considerable to be counted.

Courage and daring, no matter how mad and ungodly, have always a redundancy of vim and life to recommend them to the nether man that lies within us, and no doubt his desperate courage, his battle against the tremendous odds of all the civilized world of law and order, have had much to do in making a popular hero of our friend of the black flag. But it is not altogether courage and daring that endear him to our hearts. There is another and perhaps a greater kinship in that lust for wealth that makes one's fancy revel more pleasantly in the story of the division of treasure in the pirate's island retreat, the hiding of his godless gains somewhere in the sandy stretch of tropic beach, there to remain hidden until the time should come to rake the doubloons up again and to spend them like a lord in polite society, than in the most thrilling tales of his wonderful escapes from commissioned cruisers through tortuous channels between the coral reefs.

And what a life of adventure is his, to be sure! A life of constant alertness, constant danger, constant escape! An ocean Ishmaelite, he wanders forever aimlessly, homelessly; now unheard of for months, now careening his boat on some lonely uninhabited shore, now appearing suddenly to swoop down on some merchant vessel with rattle of musketry, shouting, yells,

Frank X. Leyendecker.

and a hell of unbridled passions let loose to rend and tear. What a Carlislean hero! What a setting of blood and lust and flame and rapine for such a hero!

Piracy, such as was practiced in the flower of its day—that is, during the early 18th century—was no sudden growth. It was an evolution, from the semi-lawful buccaneering of the 16th century, just as buccaneer-ing was upon its part, in a certain sense, an evolu-tion from the unorgan-ized, unauthorized war-fare of the Tudor period.

For there was a deal of piratical smack in the anti-Span-ish ventures of Elizabethan days. Many of the adventurers—of the Sir Francis Drake school, for instance—actually overstep-ped again and again the bounds of interna-tional law, entering into the realms of de facto piracy. Nevertheless, while their doings were not recognized officially by the gov-ernment, the perpetrators were neither punished nor reprimanded for their ex-cursions against Spanish commerce at home or in the West Indies; rather were they commended, and it was considered not altogether a discreditable thing for men to get rich upon the spoils taken from Spanish galleons in times of nominal peace. Many of the most reputable citi-zens and merchants of London, when they felt that the queen failed in her duty of pushing the fight against the great Catholic Power, fitted out fleets upon their own account and sent them to levy good Protestant war of a private nature upon the Pope's anointed.

Some of the treasures captured in such ventures were immense, stupendous, unbelievable. For an example, one can hardly credit the truth of the "purchase" gained by Drake in the famous capture of the plate ship in the South Sea.

One of the old buccaneer writers of a century later says: "The Spaniards affirm to this day that he took at that time twelvescore tons of plate and sixteen bowls of coined money a man (his number being then 45 men in

all), insomuch heave much of that they were forced to it overboard, because his ship could not carry it all."

Maybe this was a very greatly exaggerated state-ment put by the author and his Spanish authorities; nev-ertheless there was enough truth in it to prove very conclusively to the bold minds of the age that

*The pirate was fiction's badman/hero before the invention of the Western story.*

DRAWN BY GEORGE GIBBS

tremendous profits—"purchases" they called them—were to be made from piracy. The Western World is filled with the names of daring mariners of those old days, who came flitting across the great trackless ocean in their little tublike boats of a few hundred tons burden, partly to explore unknown seas, partly—largely, perhaps—in pursuit of Spanish treasure: Frobisher, Davis, Drake, and a score of others.

In this left-handed war against Catholic Spain many of the adventurers were, no doubt, stirred and incited by a grim, Calvinistic, puritanical zeal for Protestantism. But equally beyond doubt the gold and silver and plate of the "Scarlet Woman" had much to do with the persistent energy with which these hardy mariners braved the mysterious, unknown terrors of the great unknown ocean that stretched away to the sunset, there in faraway waters to attack the huge, unwieldy, treasure-laden galleons that sailed up and down the Caribbean Sea and through the Bahama Channel.

Of all ghastly and terrible things, old-time religious war was the most ghastly and terrible. One can hardly credit nowadays the cold, callous cruelty of those times. Generally death was the least penalty that capture entailed. When the Spaniards made prisoners of the English, the Inquisition took them in hand, and what that meant all the world knows. When the English captured a Spanish vessel the prisoners were tortured, either for the sake of revenge or to compel them to disclose where treasure lay hidden. Cruelty begat cruelty, and it would be hard to say whether the Anglo-Saxon or the Latin showed himself to be most proficient in torturing his victim.

When Cobham, for instance, captured the Spanish ship in the Bay of Biscay, after all resistance was over and the heat of the battle had cooled, he ordered his crew to bind the captain and all of the crew and every Spaniard aboard—whether in arms or not—to sew them up in the mainsail and to fling them overboard. There were some 20 dead bodies in the sail when a few days later it was washed up on the shore.

Of course such acts were not likely to go unavenged, and many an innocent life was sacrificed to pay the debt of Cobham's cruelty.

Nothing could be more piratical than all this. Nevertheless, as was said, it was winked at, condoned, if not sanctioned, by the law; and it was not beneath people of family and respectability to take part in it. But by and by Protestantism and Catholicism began to be at somewhat less deadly enmity with each other; religious wars were still far enough from being ended, but the scabbard of the sword was no longer flung away when the blade was drawn. And so followed a time of nominal peace, and a generation arose with whom it was no longer respectable and worthy—one might say a matter of duty—to fight a country with which one's own land was not at war. Nevertheless, the seed had been sown; it had been demonstrated that it was feasible to practice piracy against Spain and not to suffer therefor. Blood had been shed and cruelty practiced, and, once indulged, no lust seems stronger than that of shedding blood and practicing cruelty.

Though Spain might be ever so well grounded in peace at home, in the West Indies she was always at war with the whole world—English, French, Dutch. It was almost a matter of life or death with her to keep the hold she had upon the New World. At home she was bankrupt and, upon the earthquake of the Reformation, her power was already beginning to totter and to crumble to

pieces. America was her treasure house, and from it alone could she hope to keep her leaking purse full of gold and silver. So it was that she strove strenuously, even desperately, to keep out the rest of the world from her American possessions—a bootless task, for the old order upon which her power rested was broken and crumbled forever. But still she strove, fighting against fate, and so it was that in

*Like the Western badman, the pirate was supposed to hide a warm heart under his fierce exterior.*

the tropical America it was one continual war between her and all the world. Thus it came that, long after piracy ceased to be allowed at home, it continued in those faraway seas with unabated vigor, recruiting to its service all that lawless malign element which gathers together in every newly opened country where the only law is lawlessness, where might is right, and where a living is to be gained with no more trouble than cutting a throat.

Norman
Rockwell

# The Glory of the Sea

## BY JAN DE HARTOG

## The Atlantic

There is a South Atlantic and there is a North Atlantic, but only the Northern one is unique. The South Atlantic is a watered-down version of the Pacific and the Indian Ocean. It is neither the sea on which every point of the compass holds a different promise, like the Indian Ocean, nor man's nearest experience to eternity, like the Pacific. It is like the big square in a provincial town—smaller than others and bigger than some. It looks and feels as if it were a substitute for something; apart from the trade winds and the doldrums, the South Atlantic is just any sea until one reaches the Horn.

The trades, so the young sailor will find, make him uneasy; they just cannot be true.

For the same wind to blow at the same strength from the same direction forever is, strangely enough, the very reverse of relaxing. The doldrums, important in the days of sail, have now lost their menace, except to lifeboats.

It is only in the North Atlantic that man is forever faced by Oceanus in his might. No two days are the same: gales of incredible violence, days of supernatural glassy calm, red skies, green skies, blue skies, and the fantastic northern lights make the sailor realize he is fighting an alien element.

It is not for nothing that of all the great explorers, Columbus is the most famous, for ever since antiquity the Atlantic has been the threshold to the edge of the world. All fantastic stories, from sea serpents to the Aldebaran and Atlantis, have come from the Atlantic, and no one who has not sailed that incredible sea knows what it means to be a sailor. All other oceans have their schedule: the Indian Ocean has a bad period and a good

J. J. GOULD

*In the 1700s, ships from Nantucket and New Bedford pursued the sperm whale in the South Atlantic. By 1800 they were moving on to still richer whaling grounds in the Pacific.*

one, the Pacific gives ample warning of its mood, even the Mediterranean harbors few surprises to the experienced navigator. Only the Atlantic is completely and

*A storm is always brewing somewhere in the cold and windy North Atlantic. Painting by A. O. Fischer.*

utterly unpredictable, despite all the solemn studies written about her character that try to make sense of her streaks of madness and her incomparable moments of majesty.

All the adjectives used to describe the sea since the beginning of man's consciousness can be applied to the Atlantic. The only way to predict her aspect for tonight is to write all those adjectives on separate bits of paper, roll them into little balls, put them in a tin, shake them, and let the cabin boy draw. It may be "azure" and it may be "fickle"; it may be "terrifying" and it may be "pewter"; the only safe ones are "deep" and "wet."

To those reared on the North Atlantic every sea change will be a holiday.

# The North Sea

When I was young, the North Sea was the biggest sea I knew and terrifying in its might. To the youngsters of the east coast of England, the North Sea is a friend; to the ones on its opposite shores, it is fraught with menace, a never-relenting enemy. Young English boys potter around lustily with little boats and rickety old yachts in the shelter of their island; on the eastern shores of the North Sea, it is another matter.

For the prevailing winds in the North Sea are westerly and gales are frequent and sudden. Furthermore, the eastern shores are sown with banks and shifting shoals,

*Men who know the North Sea well view a calm, bright summer day with suspicion. A 1941* Post *cover by Dale Nichols.*

so, apart from courage, the young yachtsman needs a solid knowledge of navigation to go playing around in the great gray open.

The North Sea, more than any other sea I know, belongs to the fishermen, a great many of whom are Dutch. They are among the toughest and most antique of their kind. Some of them still wear their local costumes and pray to tribal gods. I sailed with them as a boy; so, to me, the North Sea stood for seasickness, cold, wet clothes, sore hands, homesickness, and the icy wrath of Yahweh. I shall never be able to give an objective description of the North Sea for that reason. There I have known my first fears and joys; my earliest dreams of love and adventure have been circled over by mewing sea gulls in a pale blue sky, and my first anticipations of eternal damnation have been shivered out in the peak of a rusty trawler as the horses of the Apocalypse came thundering by from horizon to horizon.

To the young sailor who passes through the North Sea on his way elsewhere, it will come as a surprise. The waves are steep, short, and aggressive, the currents are strong, and navigation becomes tricky because of the shoals of fishermen and the intense traffic, which turns the Channel into a village main street on Fair day. The fishermen are worse in their disdain for intruders than anywhere else. If they show lights at all at night, they show the wrong ones, and as a lot of fishing is done in pairs—two drifting luggers dragging a net between them—one should take great care not to pass between the two. For trouble on the North Sea is about the worst to be got anywhere.

On summer days the North Sea can give a somnolent feeling of security that is dangerous. Lighthouses and lightships swing their transparent scythes through the stars, garlands of colored lights festoon the distant shores and the faint glow of towns lights up the haze afar.

Yet those visions of a better world and eternal peace should be considered as highly suspect. Somewhere a gale is brewing, waiting to pounce with all the shrieks of hell, and there is little leeway to the east.

My most poignant memory of the North Sea in later years was a Christmas Eve over the Dogger Bank. I sat with the wireless operator in his cubicle on the boat deck and we listened in to the divine services of all the countries around the shores. There came a moment when they blended: prayers from Denmark, songs from Germany, bells from Holland, carols from England, sermons from Scotland, and a faint icy tinkling of handbells, shaken by children in the snow outside some Norwegian village church. I have never felt nearer to God and His benevolent bewilderment than at that moment.

If the Mediterranean is the cradle of man's culture, the Atlantic the backdrop to his daring, and the Pacific his lonely road through space, the North Sea is the convex mirror of Christianity's young struggle and melodious hope.

# The Mediterranean

This is a magnificent sea. It combines everything one dreamed of as a boy: the deep blue water, the crystalline depths, the hot sun, the white clouds over distant mountains. Every shore bears the trace of antiquity: in

*The Mediterranean is the melting pot of seas where meet men and ships of every type and time. Painting by A. O. Fischer.*

*The Pacific is vast but not empty—no sea is so full of marine life in its myriad forms. Painting by A. O. Fischer.*

the south, the Dark Ages loom from the forbidding hilltops, and on deserted beaches the antlike silhouettes of a man and a donkey trudge wearily along the shore. In the north, the orange and dark green of fir-grown cliffs and the skyline of snow-capped mountains give the sailor lost in this dream a feeling of being offered all the riches of the earth at once, like Jesus.

The keynote to the Mediterranean shores is ripeness. The fruit is bigger; the flowers, heavy with scent, bloom forever; enormous crickets rattle like dice, and prehistoric fish rise, gaping and monstrous, within sight, as in an aquarium. The people are ripe too; the centuries of strife are past; now they sit or loiter amid the cozy rubble of discarded cultures, and play games with giant iron marbles. They rarely sing, always quarrel, never fight; their life is punctuated by the slow-swinging

clatter of the wooden bead curtains that keep out the flies; and they exert a tremendous tidal pull toward their careless, lazy existence.

The off-shore dangers, apart from the reefs and rocks, are sudden violent winds that have romantic names like mistral, sirocco, and tramontane. They come literally like bolts from the blue and, in the case of the mistral, its violence is never quite realized because of the bright blue sky and the dazzling visibility. The waves are short and steep, and there are some regions marked in red on the pilot charts where crosscurrents and confused swell can sink ships without a trace. The dangers at sea are the reflection of the dangers ashore; the little islands set gemlike in the evening sky are, like the happy ripeness of life on land, offered as a temptation.

To be young and a sailor in the Mediterranean is to feel like the gods on Olympus. On going ashore, one feels like shedding one's cloak of immortality and turning into a swan. When Ulysses had himself tied to the mast after blocking the ears of his crew to the sirens' song, he wrote a most important addition to the Notices to Mariners, Mediterranean.

# The Pacific

Years ago I described in my first novel a sailor's impression on rounding the Horn and facing the Pacific for the first time in his life. I said that the waves were different, for behind them surged 25,000 miles of loneliness, and that every crew emerging into the waste of the silent ocean had a difficult time overcoming the archaic terror of man's futility in the universe. After reading the book, several old sailors wrote to me saying that for the first time they had found the Pacific truthfully described.

Yet I had never been there. All I had done was to look at a sixpenny globe atlas and realize how big it was. I have been there since and found that I was right; there is indeed something about the Pacific that makes it different from any other ocean on our planet. The description I provided as a young man was not a flash of genius; every sailor facing a waste of water which he knows to be the Pacific falls under the spell of the sixpenny globe of his own childhood.

There are things man is unable to forget. To look at a photograph of a Sphinx may make it look like one of a set of iron log supports; once he sets eyes on the real thing he will be assailed by the concentrated awe of hundreds of generations of spectators. The same goes for the Taj Mahal, Napoleon's Tomb, and Washington's spectacles. It is the magic of the countless that does its eerie work; and the Pacific,

biggest ocean of the world, is the most tinged with mankind's imagination. It is a place where vessels vanish and are perhaps still sailing between water and wind. It is a desert full of ghosts, and on its trailless plain more dreams and memories course than there are shooting stars in an August night. For beyond the silver horizon lies modern man's new paradise—the islands.

People who have actually been there rarely dream about living on a Pacific island. They are not fragments of paradise; they are outsize cradles. If modern man thinks of a return to the satin and the faint smell of powder of babyhood as bliss, the Pacific islands are indeed the answer. To lie on his back, pint-sized, facing the lazy choice between his toes and the dangling rattle is the real image of man in the South Pacific paradise. For the guitar-strumming beauties in their grass skirts are oddly sexless, once one sets eyes on them, and the

*It is only fair that the islands of the Pacific— and their inhabitants— should be beautiful. They are so small, those islands, and so far apart in the largest of all the oceans.*

eternal song of the surf underneath the tropical sky has the disadvantage that it is eternal. On these conditions bliss is the best working description of hell I can think of.

The ocean itself, however, will give the young sailor an unforgettable experience. By its sheer size it brings home to him the tempo of life at sea. To sail for weeks upon weeks without anything in sight but the water, the sky, and the snub nose of his vessel slowly rising and falling, will set him musing in his diary about things he has so far ignored because of his eager expectancy of land to be sighted at dawn. He will write, "I wonder

northwest cradle the sailor on a sea of turquoise between November and April, whereas from May to October he is buffeted and maddened by squalls and calms from the south. This goes for the whole of the Indian Ocean in varying degrees, and the contrasts are so strong as to be hard to believe. There are months in which one might as well be sailing the North Atlantic, snarling and gray, with low ragged cloud, and there are months of such unearthly beauty that it has taken Conrad a lifetime to describe it.

The young sailor entering the Indian Ocean in the good period will realize that he has never known there

whether perhaps I am idealizing Maggie," which is the first step on the road that took the great philosophers of mankind out of sight of the foot-slogging army.

When at last land is sighted, and the pilot or the harbormaster climbs on board, he will have the strangest experience of all: he will feel an inexpressible mixture of relief and regret.

# The Indian Ocean

There are two Indian Oceans—one between November and April, and one between May and October. The two are so different that the Indian Ocean frequently becomes the cause of heated quarrels in fo'c'sles and messrooms, when those who know it contradict one another with the violence of conviction. In the Arabian Sea, for instance, winds are mainly southwest from June to August, reaching gale force on eight to ten days a month. From November to April, light to moderate northeasterly winds prevail. Between Suvadiva, in the south of the Maldive Islands, and the west coast of Sumatra, light to moderate winds between west and

were so many brilliant stars in the sky. The whole night dome, of dark blue velvet, seems to have turned into one colossal Milky Way, and the Milky Way itself is a dazzling furrow plowed through the universe. The sea has an oily quality that is not encountered anywhere else on earth. It breathes slowly, like a sleeper, with a long, cradling swell and the ship's wake mirrors the Milky Way. Strange luminous shapes glide silently underneath the glassy surface, squids rise like fiery rockets from the depths, and occasionally, in very still nights, the young sailor will feel as if touched by a magic wand and turn into Sindbad, when in the darkness a whale roars or a dolphin splashes.

The Indian Ocean in the calm season is a sea of dreams. To stand on the bridge at night and watch the world makes the sailor feel young and immortal. His future is brilliant, his past fortunate, his sweetheart the greatest stroke of luck any man ever had, and they say that women show their breasts in Bali. He will think of leading the life of a planter; he will look forward to all his boyhood books of adventure coming true. Above all, he will be happy to be himself.

Then when the land of promise is first discerned by a strange, nutty smell, he will head for those waiting for him with a completely guileless mind. The magic will last until he either sails home in the gale season or sights the white miracle of Aden. Until then, the carpet he bought will be Persian, the brass idol gold, the small

Javanese rice picker sculptured in teakwood a work of art, and the earrings of conscience will be jade. Seldom will a traveler have brought home more worthless junk and a better notion of the richness of life.

*From the Indian Ocean a young sailor carried home exotic gifts and tall tales. A 1930* Post *cover by Norman Rockwell.*

# Why Bell-Bottoms?

There is, of course, a perfectly good reason why the trousers of the traditional sailor's uniform are extra wide at the bottom.

There is a reason for almost every feature of the picturesque garb the U.S. Navy abandoned in the 1960s, though some of the reasons date back to sailing-ship days and may seem less than totally relevant today in a Navy that has radar and computers and diesel engines rather than ropes and canvas.

The bell-bottoms made it easy for the seaman to roll up his trousers and thereby keep them dry when he scrubbed—or rather, swabbed—the decks.

These remarkable trousers button at both sides rather than at center front—because center buttons would be more likely to catch on ropes when the man climbed the ship's rigging. At one time, U.S. Navy

bell-bottoms fastened with 13 buttons to commemorate the 13 original states.

When properly pressed, bell-bottoms have reverse creases along the side seams. They hold this crease perfectly, even in damp sea air, when turned wrong side out, rolled snugly, and then tucked in the sailor's seabag. Try *that* with ordinary front-creased trousers!

The top—generally called the jumper—pulls over the head for the same reason the bell-bottoms button at the sides: Center-front buttons would be a nuisance, frequently tangled in the ship's ropes and torn off. The three rows of white braid around collar and cuffs appeared first on British Navy uniforms, and are said to commemorate three great naval victories—the Baltic, Nile, and Trafalgar. The odd-shaped collar, like a squared-off bib worn backwards, served to protect the rest of the uniform from tar that the British sailor smeared onto his pigtails.

The jaunty tie knotted under the collar is actually an oversize handkerchief rolled on the diagonal. It hangs there, within convenient wiping distance of sweaty brow or running nose, and doesn't make an unsightly bulge in the sailor's pocket. Why a black hanky? Tradition says they were white until the British Navy mourned the death of Nelson.

We come, then, to the sailor's cap of stiffly-stitched white canvas. Like jumper and bell-bottoms, it is designed to roll up and pack snugly in a seabag, and it is also designed to cling to the wearer's head in winds that would tear off any hat with a brim or visor. But that's not all. Flip the cuff down and the cap becomes a canvas pail. Very handy for carrying drinking water, or for bailing out a lifeboat.

In 1977, U.S. Navy men voted in favor of a return to the traditional "sailor suit." One reason: The more modern coat-and-pants uniform with visored cap had proved difficult to care for on board ship, where closet space is meager or nonexistent. Another reason: Tradition has it that girls find the sailor in bell-bottoms irresistible!

*Lawrence Toney*

*They looked so jaunty! One expected every sailor to tap-dance as well as Gene Kelly.*

JOHN E. SHERIDAN

*By the 30's, most sailors wore dungarees at work aboard ship—but they still looked like sailors when they went ashore in whites.*

# Saltwater Poems

## The Tide Rises, the Tide Falls

The tide rises, the tide falls,
The twilight darkens, the curlew calls;
Along the sea-sands damp and brown
The traveler hastens toward the town;
 And the tide rises, the tide falls.

Darkness settles on roofs and walls,
But the sea in the darkness calls and calls;
The little waves, with their soft white hands,
Efface the footprints in the sands,
 And the tide rises, the tide falls.

The morning breaks; the steeds in their stalls
Stamp and neigh, as the hostler calls;
The day returns; but nevermore
Returns the traveler to the shore,
 And the tide rises, the tide falls.

HENRY WADSWORTH LONGFELLOW

## Sails

Those graceful wings
of constant changing beauty
lovely on every point of sailing
in every mood of weather, calm or storm.
Those perfect forms of ever changing curves
that grace the summer seas around our coast
enhancing the very scene that Nature paints.
Skimming over sparkling waters, filled
by gentle breezes
or mirrored in glassy calms,
drooping canvas casting crazy patterns
on the water.
Or, double-reefed, heeling to a summer gale,
drenched with spray from angry crested waves
and flying home to shelter.
Kissed by the sun's bright rays
and racing with the clouds,
or, etched against gray banks of
threatening rain-clouds
which warn of squalls to come.
Close-hauled, sheets pinn'd hard home,
beating to the weather mark,

or, sheets eased off and bow waves hissing
as they reached along the shore.
Then, running free before light airs
gliding gently, soundless,
booms squared off and listless sagging sheets,
silken spinnakers shimmering in the sun,
or billowing out at the coming of a breeze;
soon all sheets taut again and pulling hard,
each sail in sun and ever moving shadow,
with nuances of light and shade . . .
A symphony of curves.

IAN G. GILCHRIST

## At the Seaside

When I was down beside the sea
A wooden spade they gave to me
 To dig the sandy shore.

My holes were empty like a cup.
In every hole the sea came up,
 Till it could come no more.

ROBERT LOUIS STEVENSON

## In Cabin'd Ships at Sea

In cabin'd ships at sea,
The boundless blue on every side expanding,
With whistling winds and music of the waves,
 the large imperious waves,
Or some long bark buoy'd on the dense marine,
Where joyous, full of faith, spreading white sails,
She cleaves the ether mid the sparkle and the foam
 of day, or under many a star at night,
By sailors young and old haply will I,
 a reminiscence of the land, be read,
In full rapport at last.

*Here are our thoughts, voyagers' thoughts,*
*Here not the land, firm land, alone appears,*
 *may then by them be said,*
*The sky o'erarches here, we feel the*
 *undulating deck beneath our feet,*
*We feel the long pulsation, ebb and flow of endless*
 *motion,*
*The tones of unseen mystery, the vague, and vast*
 *suggestions of the briny world, the liquid-*
 *flowing syllables,*
*The perfume, the faint creaking of the cordage,*

*the melancholy rhythm,*
*The boundless vista and the horizon far and*
*dim are all here,*
*And this is ocean's poem.*

Then falter not, O book, fulfill your destiny,
You not a reminiscence of the land alone,
You too as a lone bark cleaving the ether,
   purpos'd I know not whither, yet ever full of faith,

Consort to every ship that sails, sail you!
Bear forth to them folded my love (dear marines, for
   you I fold it here in every leaf);
Speed on my book! spread your white sails, my
   little bark, athwart the imperious waves,
Chant on, sail on, bear o'er the boundless blue
   from me to every sea,
This song for mariners and all their ships.

                   WALT WHITMAN

*Poised sailors—she with pompadour barely windblown, he with his pipe drawing nicely—appeared on the* Post *in 1906.*

*The sturdy New England fishing boat called a Gloucesterman forms the background of this 1934 painting by Gordon Grant.*

# Sea-Fever

I must go down to the seas again. to the lonely sea
    and the sky,
And all I ask is a tall ship and a star to steer her by,
And the wheel's kick and the wind's song and the
    white sail's shaking,
And a gray mist on the sea's face and a gray dawn
    breaking.

I must go down to the seas again, for the call of the
    running tide
Is a wild call and a clear call that may not be denied;
And all I ask is a windy day with the white
    clouds flying,
And the flung spray and the blown spume and the
    sea gulls crying.

I must go down to the seas again, to the lonely sea
    and the sky,
To the gull's way and the whale's way where the
    wind's like a whetted knife;
And all I ask is a merry yarn from a laughing
    fellow rover,
And quiet sleep and a sweet dream when the long
    trick's over.

                JOHN MASEFIELD

# After the Sea Ship

After the sea ship, after the whistling winds,
After the white-gray sails taut to their spars and ropes,
Below, a myriad myriad waves hastening,
    lifting up their necks,
Tending in ceaseless flow toward the track of the ship,
Waves of the ocean bubbling and gurgling,
    blithely prying,
Waves, undulating waves, liquid, uneven,
    emulous waves,
Toward that whirling current, laughing and
    buoyant, with curves,
Where the great vessel sailing and tacking
    displaced the surface,
Larger and smaller waves in the spread of the
    ocean yearnfully flowing,
The wake of the sea ship after she passes,
    flashing and frolicsome under the sun,
A motley procession with many a fleck of foam
    and many fragments,

Following the stately and rapid ship, in the
    wake following.

                WALT WHITMAN

# The Sea Gypsy

I am fevered with the sunset,
I am fretful with the bay,
For the wander-thirst is on me
And my soul is in Cathay.

There's a schooner in the offing,
With her topsails shot with fire,
And my heart has gone aboard her
For the Islands of Desire.

I must forth again tomorrow!
With the sunset I must be
Hull down on the trail of rapture
In the wonder of the sea.

                RICHARD HOVEY

# The Inchcape Rock

No stir in the air, no stir in the sea—
The ship was as still as she could be;
Her sails from heaven received no motion;
Her keel was steady in the ocean.

Without either sign or sound of their shock,
The waves flowed over the Inchcape rock;
So little they rise, so little they fell,
They did not move the Inchcape bell.

The holy Abbot of Aberbrothok
Had placed that bell on the Inchcape rock;
On a buoy in the storm it floated and swung
And over the waves it warning rung.

When the rock was hid by the surges' swell,
The mariners heard the warning bell;
And then they knew the perilous rock,
And blessed the Abbot of Aberbrothok.

The sun in heaven was shining gay—
All things were joyful on that day;
The seabirds screamed as they wheeled around,
And there was joyance in their sound.

The buoy of the Inchcape bell was seen,
A darker speck on the ocean green;
Sir Ralph, the rover, walked his deck,
And he fixed his eyes on the darker speck.

His eye was on the bell and float:
Quoth he, "My men, put out the boat;
And row me to the Inchcape rock,
And I'll plague the priest of Aberbrothok."

The boat is lowered, the boatmen row,
And to the Inchcape rock they go;
Sir Ralph bent over from the boat,
And cut the warning bell from the float.

Down sank the bell with a gurgling sound;
The bubbles rose, and burst around.
Quoth Sir Ralph,
    "The next who comes to the rock
Will not bless the Abbot of Aberbrothok."

Sir Ralph, the rover, sailed away—
He scoured the seas for many a day;
And now, grown rich with plundered store,
He steers his course to Scotland's shore.

So thick a haze o'erspreads the sky
They cannot see the sun on high;
The wind hath blown a gale all day;
At evening it hath died away.

On the deck the rover takes his stand;
So dark it is they see no land.
Quoth Sir Ralph, "It will be lighter soon,
For there is the dawn of the rising moon."

"Canst hear," said one, "the breakers roar?
For yonder, methinks, should be the shore.
Now where we are I cannot tell,
But I wish we could hear the Inchcape bell."

They hear no sound; the swell is strong;
Though the wind hath fallen, they drift along;
Till the vessel strikes with a shivering shock—
O Christ! it is the Inchcape rock!

Sir Ralph, the rover, tore his hair;
He cursed himself in his despair.
The waves rush in on every side;
The ship is sinking beneath the tide.

But ever in his dying fear
One dreadful sound he seemed to hear—
A sound as if with the Inchcape bell
The Devil below was ringing his knell.

ROBERT SOUTHEY

By Writers
Who
Went
to
Sea

# Under the Deck Awnings

### A STORY BY JACK LONDON

*He would have been called a juvenile delinquent if the term had existed in 1893. A school dropout, he roamed Oakland with a tough street gang, became involved in petty crime, and was often in trouble with the law. He also learned to sail a tiny skiff on the treacherous waters of San Francisco Bay. A turning point in Jack London's life occurred a few days after his seventeenth birthday when he signed aboard a three-masted schooner bound for the Arctic sealing grounds. Life*

*aboard ship gave him a taste of success, self-confidence, and an unshakable desire to write. This story appeared in the* Post *in 1910.*

"Can any man—a gentleman, I mean—call a woman a pig?" The little man flung this challenge forth to the whole group, then leaned back in his deck chair, sipping lemonade with an air commingled of certitude and watchful belligerence. Nobody made answer. They were used to the little man and his sudden passions and high elevations.

"I repeat, it was in my presence that he said a certain lady, whom none of you knows, was a pig. He did not say swine. He grossly said that she was a pig. And I hold that no man who is a man could possibly make such a remark about any woman."

Doctor Dawson puffed stolidly at his black pipe. Matthews, with knees hunched up and clasped by his arms, was absorbed in the flight of a guny. Sweet, finishing his Scotch and soda, was questing about with his eyes for a deck steward.

"I ask you, Mr. Treloar, can any man call any woman a pig?"

Treloar, who happened to be sitting next to him, was startled by the abruptness of the attack, and wondered what grounds he had ever given the little man to believe that he could call a woman a pig.

"I should say," he began his hesitant answer, "that it—er—depends on the—er—the lady."

The little man was aghast.

"You mean——" he quavered.

"That I have seen female humans who were as bad as pigs—and worse."

There was a long, painful silence. The little man seemed withered by the coarse brutality of the reply. In his face was unutterable hurt and woe.

"You have told of a man who made a not nice remark, and you have classified him," Treloar said in cold, even tones. "I shall now tell you about a woman—I beg your pardon—a lady—and when I have finished I shall ask you to classify her. Miss Caruthers I shall call her, principally for the reason that it is not her name. It was on a P. & O. boat, and it occurred several years ago.

"Miss Caruthers was charming. No; that is not the word. She was amazing. She was a young woman and a lady. Her father was a certain high official whose name, if I mentioned it, would be immediately recognized by all of you. She was with her mother and two maids at the time, going out to join the old gentleman wherever you like to wish in the East.

"She—and pardon me for repeating—was amazing. It is the one adequate word. Even the most minor adjectives applicable to her are bound to be sheer superlatives. There was nothing she could not do better than

*Jack London wrote of a transition period when steam and sail met at sea, when women were still very much ladies in their long skirts and high collars but no longer Victorian "clinging vines." On the opposite page, an Anton Otto Fischer illustration. Above, a 1902* Post *cover.*

any woman and than most men. Sing, play—bah!—as some rhetorician once said of old Nap, competition fled from her. Swim! She could have made a fortune and a name as a public performer. She was one of those rare women who can strip off all the frills of dress and in a simple swimming suit be more satisfyingly beautiful. Dress! She was an artist. Her taste was unerring.

"But her swimming. Physically, she was the perfect woman—you know what I mean; not in the gross, muscular way of acrobats, but in all the delicacy of line and fragility of frame and texture; and combined with this, strength. How she could do it was the marvel. You know the wonder of a woman's arm—the forearm, I mean; the sweet fading away from rounded biceps and hint of muscle, down through small elbow and firm, soft swell to the wrist, small—unthinkably small and round and strong? This was hers. And yet, to see her swimming the sharp, quick English overhand stroke, and getting somewhere with it too, was—well, I understand anatomy and athletics and such things, and yet it was a mystery to me how she could do it.

"She could stay underwater for two minutes. I have timed her. No man on board, except Dennitson, could capture as many coins as she with a single dive. On the forward main deck was a big canvas tank with six feet of seawater. We used to toss small coins into it. I have seen her dive from the bridge deck—no mean feat in

*"She ran the ship, she ran the voyage, she ran everything."*

itself—into that six feet of water and fetch up no less than 47 coins, scattered at random over the whole bottom of the tank. Dennitson, a quiet young Englishman, never exceeded her in this, though he made it a point always to tie her score.

"She was a sea-woman, true. But she was a land-woman, a horsewoman—a—she was the universal woman. To see her, all softness of flowing dress, surrounded by half a dozen eager men, languidly careless of them, or flashing brightness and wit on them and at them and through them, one would fancy she was good for nothing else in the world. At such moments I have compelled myself to remember her score of 47 coins from the bottom of the swimming tank. But that was she—the everlasting wonder of a woman who did all things well.

"She fascinated every betrousered human around her. She had me—and I don't mind confessing it—she had me to heel along with the rest. Young puppies and old gray dogs who ought to have known better—oh, they all came up and crawled round her skirts and whined and fawned when she whistled. They were all guilty, from young Ardmore, a pink cherub of 19, outward bound for some clerkship in the consular service, to old Captain Bentley, grizzled and seaworn, and as emotional, to look at, as a Chinese joss. There was a nice middle-aged chap, Perkins, I believe, who forgot his wife was on board until Miss Caruthers sent him to the right-about and back where he belonged.

"Men were wax in her hands. She melted them, or softly molded them, or incinerated them, as she pleased. There wasn't a steward, even, grand and remote as

*"She fascinated every betrousered human around her."*

*Jack London's Miss Caruthers might have looked like this*          *beguiling beauty, drawn for a 1904* Post *cover.*

she was, who at her bidding would have hesitated to souse the Old Man himself with a plate of soup. You have all seen such women—a sort of world's desire to all men. As a man-conqueror she was supreme. She was a whiplash, a sting and a flame, an electric spark. Oh, believe me, at times there were flashes of a will that scorched through her beauty and seduction and smote a victim into blank and shivering idiocy and fear!

"And don't fail to mark, in the light of what is to come, that she was a prideful woman: pride of race, pride of caste, pride of sex, pride of power—she had it all, a pride strange and willful and terrible.

"She ran the ship, she ran the voyage, she ran everything—and she ran Dennitson. That he had outdistanced the pack even the least wise of us admitted. That

she liked him, and that this feeling was growing, there was not a doubt. I am certain that she looked on him with kinder eyes than she had ever looked with on man before. We still worshiped and were always hanging about waiting to be whistled up, though we knew that Dennitson was laps and laps ahead of us. What might have happened we shall never know, for we came to Colombo and something else happened.

"You know Colombo, and how the native boys dive for coins in the shark-infested bay? Of course it is only among the ground sharks and fish sharks that they venture. It is almost uncanny the way they know sharks and can sense the presence of a real killer—a tiger shark, for instance, or a gray nurse strayed up from Australian waters. But let such a shark appear and, long before the passengers can guess, every mother's son of them is out of the water in a wild scramble for safety.

"It was just after tiffin and Miss Caruthers was holding her usual court under the deck awnings. Old Captain Bentley had just been whistled up and had granted her what he had never granted before—nor since—permission for the boys to come up on the promenade deck. You see, Miss Caruthers was a swimmer and she was interested. She took up a collection of all our small change and herself tossed it overside, singly and in handfuls, arranging the terms of the contests, chiding a miss, giving extra rewards to clever wins; in short, managing the whole exhibition.

"She was especially keen on their jumping. You know, jumping feet-first from a height, it is very difficult to hold the body perpendicularly while in the air. The center of gravity of the human body is high, and the tendency is to overtopple, but the little beggars employed a method new to her, which she desired to learn. Leaping from the davits of the boat deck above, they plunged downward, their faces and shoulders bowed forward looking at the water; and only at the last moment did they abruptly straighten up and enter the water erect and true.

"It was a pretty sight. Their diving was not so good, though there was one of them who was excellent at it, as he was at all the other stunts. Some white man must

have taught him, for he made the proper swan dive and did it as beautifully as I have ever seen it done. You know, it is headfirst into the water; and from a great height the problem is to enter the water at the perfect angle. Miss the angle and it means at the least a twisted back and injury for life. Also, it has meant death for many a bungler. This boy could do it—70 feet I know he cleared in one dive from the rigging—clenched hands on chest, head thrown back, sailing more like a bird, upward and out, and out and down, body flat on the air, so that if it struck the surface in that position it would be split in half like a herring. But the moment before the water is reached the head drops forward, the hands go out and lock the arms in an arch in advance of the head, and the body curves gracefully downward and enters the water just right.

"This the boy did again and again to the delight of all of us, but particularly of Miss Caruthers. He could not have been a moment over 12 or 13, yet he was by far the cleverest of the gang. He was the favorite of his crowd and its leader. Though there were many older than he, they acknowledged his chieftaincy. He was a beautiful boy, a lithe young god in breathing bronze, eyes wide apart, intelligent and daring—a bubble, a mote, a beautiful flash and sparkle of life. You have seen wonderfully glorious creatures—animals, anything, a leopard, a horse—restless, eager, too much alive ever to be still, silken of muscle, each slightest movement a benediction of grace, every action wild, untrammeled, and over all spilling out that intense vitality, that sheen and luster of living light. The boy had it. Life poured out of him almost in an effulgence. His skin glowed with it. It burned in his eyes. I swear I could

*Animal artist Charles Livingston Bull drew this shark pursuing a giant ray in 1910.*

*Marine artist Anton Otto Fischer painted steamers as well as sailing craft; like London and Conrad, he found beauty everywhere at sea.*

almost hear it crackle from him. Looking at him, it was as if a whiff of ozone came to one's nostrils—so fresh and young was he, so resplendent with health, so wildly wild.

"This was the boy, and it was he who gave the alarm in the midst of the sport. The boys made a dash of it for the gangway platform, swimming the fastest strokes they knew, pell-mell, floundering and splashing, fright in their faces, clambering out with jumps and surges, any way to get out, lending one another a hand to safety, till all were strung along the gangway and peering down into the water.

" 'What is the matter?' asked Miss Caruthers.

" 'A shark, I fancy,' Captain Bentley answered. 'Lucky little beggars that he didn't get one of them.'

" 'Are they afraid of sharks?' she asked.

" 'Aren't you?' he asked back.

"She shuddered, looked overside at the water, and made a *moue*.

" 'Not for the world would I venture where a shark

might be,' she said, and shuddered again. 'They are horrible! Horrible!'

"The boys came up on the promenade deck, clustering close to the rail and worshiping Miss Caruthers, who had flung them such a wealth of bakshish. The performance being over, Captain Bentley motioned to them to clear out; but she stopped him.

" 'One moment, please, Captain. I have always understood that the natives are not afraid of sharks.'

"She beckoned the boy of the swan dive nearer to her and signed to him to dive over again. He shook his head and, along with all his crew behind him, laughed as if it were a good joke.

" 'Shark,' he volunteered, pointing to the water.

" 'No!' she said. 'There is no shark.'

"But he nodded his head positively and the boys behind him nodded with equal positiveness.

" 'No, no, no!' she cried. And then to us: 'Who'll lend me a half crown and a sovereign?'

"Immediately the half dozen of us were presenting

her with half crowns and sovereigns, and she accepted the two coins from young Ardmore.

"She held up the half crown for the boys to see, but there was no eager rush to the rail preparatory to leaping. They stood there grinning sheepishly. She offered the coin to each one individually, and each, as his turn came, rubbed his foot against his calf, shook his head, and grinned. Then she tossed the half crown overboard. With wistful, regretful faces they watched its silver flight through the air, but not one moved to follow it.

" 'Don't do it with the sovereign,' Dennitson said to her in a low voice.

"She took no notice, but held up the gold coin before the eyes of the boy of the swan dive.

" 'Don't!' said Captain Bentley. 'I wouldn't throw a sick cat overside with a shark around.'

"But she laughed, bent on her purpose, and continued to dazzle the boy.

" 'Don't tempt him,' Dennitson urged. 'It is a fortune to him and he might go over after it.'

" 'Wouldn't you?' she flared at him. 'If I threw it?' This last more softly.

"Dennitson shook his head.

" 'Your price is high,' she said. 'For how many sovereigns would you go?'

" 'There are not enough coined to get me overside,' was his answer.

"She debated a moment, the boy forgotten in her tilt with Dennitson.

" 'For me?' she said very softly.

" 'To save your life—yes; but not otherwise.'

"She turned back to the boy. Again she held the coin before his eyes, dazzling him with the vastness of its value. Then she made as if to toss it out, and involuntarily he made a half movement toward the rail, but was

checked by sharp cries of reproof from his companions. There was anger in their voices as well.

" 'I know it is only fooling,' Dennitson said. 'Carry it as far as you like, but for Heaven's sake don't throw it.'

"Whether it was that strange willfulness of hers, or whether she doubted the boy could be persuaded, there is no telling. It was unexpected to all of us. Out from the shade of the awning the coin flashed golden in the blaze of sunshine and fell toward the sea in a glittering arch. Before a hand could stay him the boy was over the rail and curving beautifully downward after the coin. Both were in the air at the same time. It was a pretty sight. The sovereign cut the water sharply, and at the very spot, almost at the same instant with scarcely a splash, the boy entered.

"From the quicker-eyed black boys watching came an exclamation. We were all at the rail. Don't tell me it is necessary for a shark to turn on its back. That one didn't. In the clear water, from the height we were above it, we saw everything. The shark was a big brute and with one drive he cut the boy squarely in half.

"There was a murmur or something from among us—who made it I did not know; it might have been I. And then there was a silence. Miss Caruthers was the first to speak. Her face was deathly white.

" 'I—I never dreamed!' she said, and laughed a short, hysterical laugh.

"All her pride was at work to give her control. She turned weakly toward Dennitson, and then on from one to another of us. In her eyes was a terrible sickness and her lips were trembling. We were brutes—oh, I know it, now that I look back upon it; but we did nothing!

" 'Mr. Dennitson,' she said—'Tom, won't you take me below?'

"He never changed the direction of his gaze, which was the bleakest I have ever seen in a man's face; nor did he move an eyelid. He took a cigarette from his case and lighted it. Captain Bentley made a nasty sound in his throat and spat overboard. That was all—that and the silence.

"She turned away and started to walk firmly down the deck. Twenty feet away she swayed and thrust a hand against the wall; and so she went on, supporting herself against the cabins and walking very slowly."

Treloar ceased. He turned his head and favored the little man with a look of cold inquiry. "Well?" he said finally. "Classify her."

The little man gulped and swallowed.

"I have nothing to say," he said. "Nothing whatever to say."

# First Days at Sea

## BY RICHARD HENRY DANA

*Young and handsome, the son of a distinguished New England family, Dana was a student at Harvard when an attack of measles left him with impaired sight. He left school and signed on the brig* Pilgrim *for a two-year cruise to California, on the hunch that a life of hard labor in the open, away from books, might restore his health and his eyesight. The story has a happy ending, because Dana was able to return to Harvard and to go on to a distinguished career as an attorney specializing in admiralty law. He also wrote a book that called attention to the hard conditions of life at sea and led to much-needed reforms and new emphasis on the seaman's legal rights. Dana went to sea in 1834; his* Two Years Before the Mast, *from which this excerpt is taken, was published in 1840.*

*The* Pilgrim *was a brigantine—two-masted and square-rigged.*

The first day we passed at sea was the Sabbath. I, being in the starboard or second mate's watch, had the opportunity of keeping the first watch, and I felt for the first time the perfect silence of the sea. The officer was walking the quarterdeck, where I had no right to go, one or two men were talking on the forecastle, whom I had little inclination to join, so that I was left open to the full impression of everything about me. However much I was affected by the beauty of the sea, the bright stars, and the clouds driven swiftly over them, I could not but remember that I was separating myself from all the social and intellectual enjoyments of life. Yet, strange as it may seem, I did then and afterward take pleasure in these reflections, hoping by them to prevent my becoming insensible to the value of what I was leaving.

But all my dreams were soon put to flight by an order from the officer to trim the yards, as the wind was getting ahead; and I could plainly see by the looks the sailors occasionally cast to windward, and by the dark clouds that were fast coming up, that we had bad weather to prepare for, and had heard the captain say that he expected to be in the Gulf Stream by twelve o'clock. In a few minutes eight bells were struck, the watch called, and we went below. I now began to feel the first discomforts of a sailor's life. The steerage in which I lived was filled with coils of rigging, spare sails, old junk, and ship stores which had not been stowed away. Moreover, there had been no berths built for us to sleep in, and we were not allowed to drive nails to hang our clothes on. The sea, too, had risen, the vessel was rolling heavily, and everything was pitched about in grand confusion. There was a complete "hurrah's nest," as the sailors say, "everything on top and nothing at hand." A large hawser had been coiled away on my chest; my hats, boots, mattress, and blankets had all "fetched away" and gone over to leeward, and were jammed and broken under the boxes and coils of rigging. To crown all, we were allowed no light to find anything with, and I was just beginning to feel strong symptoms of seasickness, and that listlessness and inactivity which accompany it. Giving up all attempts to collect my things together, I lay down on the sails, expecting every moment to hear the cry of "All hands ahoy!" which the approaching storm would soon make necessary. I shortly heard the raindrops falling on deck, thick and fast, and the watch evidently had their hands full of work, for I could hear the loud and repeated orders of the mate, the trampling of feet, the creaking of blocks, and all the accompaniments of a coming storm. In a few minutes the slide of the hatch was thrown back, which let down the noise and tumult of the deck still louder, the loud cry of "All hands ahoy! Tumble up here and take in sail!" saluted our ears, and the hatch was quickly shut again. When I got on deck, a new scene and a new experience were before me. The little brig was close-hauled upon the wind, and lying over, as it then seemed to me, nearly upon her beam ends. The heavy head sea was beating against her bows with the noise and force almost of a sledge hammer, and flying over the deck, drenching us completely through. The topsail halyards had been let go, and the great sails were filling out and backing against the masts with a noise like thunder. The wind was whistling through the rigging, loose ropes were flying about; loud and, to me, unintelligible orders constantly given and rapidly executed; and the sailors "singing out" at the ropes in their hoarse and peculiar strains. In addition to all this, I had not got my "sea legs on," was dreadfully sick, with hardly strength enough to hold on to anything, and it was "pitch-dark." This was my state when I was ordered aloft for the first time, to reef topsails.

How I got along I cannot now remember. I "laid out" on the yards and held on with all my strength. I could not have been of much service, for I remember having been sick several times before I left the topsail yard. Soon all was snug aloft, and we were again allowed to go below. This I did not consider much of a favor, for the confusion of everything below, and that inexpressible sickening smell caused by the shaking up of the bilge water in the hold, made the steerage but an indifferent refuge from the cold, wet decks. I had often read of the nautical experiences of others, but I felt as

though there could be none worse than mine; for in addition to every other evil, I could not but remember that this was only the first night of a two years' voyage. . . .

There is a witchery in the sea, its songs and stories, and in the mere sight of a ship and the sailor's dress, especially to a young mind, which has done more to man navies and fill merchantmen than all the press gangs of Europe. I have known a young man with such a passion for the sea that the very creaking of a block stirred up his imagination so that he could hardly keep his feet on dry ground; and many are the boys in every seaport who are drawn away, as by an almost irresistible attraction, from their work and schools, and hang about the decks and yards of vessels with a fondness which it is plain will have its way. No sooner, however, has the young sailor begun his new life in earnest than all this fine drapery falls off, and he learns that it is but work and hardship, after all. This is the true light in which a sailor's life is to be viewed. . . .

Notwithstanding all that has been said about the beauty of a ship under full sail, there are very few who have ever seen a ship literally under all her sail. A ship coming in or going out of port, with her ordinary sails, and perhaps two or three studding sails, is commonly said to be under full sail; but a ship never has all her sail on her except when she has a light, steady breeze very nearly, but not quite, dead aft, and so regular that it can be trusted, and is likely to last for some time. Then, with all her sails, light and heavy, and studding sails on each side, alow and aloft, she is the most glorious moving object in the world. Such a sight very few, even some who have been at sea a good deal, have ever beheld; for from the deck of your own vessel you cannot see her as you would a separate object.

One night while we were in these tropics I went out to the end of the flying jibboom on some duty, and having finished it, turned around, and lay over the

*It was unusual for a man of Dana's background to sail as an ordinary seaman, sharing damp, cramped quarters "before the mast."*

*Dana's writings forced shipowners and captains to improve the conditions under which men lived and worked at sea.*

boom for a long time, admiring the beauty of the sight before me. Being so far out from the deck, I could look at the ship as at a separate vessel and there rose up from the water, supported only by the small black hull, a pyramid of canvas, spreading out far beyond the hull, and towering up almost, as it seemed in the indistinct night air, to the clouds. The sea was as still as an inland lake; the light trade wind was gently and steadily breathing from astern; the dark-blue sky was studded with the tropical stars; there was no sound but the rippling of the water under the stem; and the sails were spread out, wide and high—the two lower studding sails stretching on each side far beyond the deck; the topmast studding sails like wings to the topsails; the topgallant studding sails spreading fearlessly out above them;

still higher, the two royal studding sails, looking like two kites flying from the same string; and highest of all, the little skysail, the apex of the pyramid, seeming actually to touch the stars, and to be out of reach of human hand. So quiet too, was the sea, and so steady the breeze, that if these sails had been sculptured marble they could not have been more motionless. Not a ripple on the surface of the canvas, not even a quivering of the extreme edges of the sail—so perfectly were they distended by the breeze. I was so lost in the sight that I forgot the presence of the man who came out with me until he said (for he too, rough old man-of-war'sman as he was, had been gazing at the show), half to himself, still looking at the marble sails, "How quietly they do their work!"

# The First Lowering of the Pequod's Boats

## BY HERMAN MELVILLE

*Melville tried clerking in a store and teaching school before he joined the crew of a merchant ship bound from New York to Liverpool. The year was 1839, and he was not quite 20 years old. Two years later, broke and unable to find other work, he signed aboard a New England whaling ship bound for Cape Horn and the Pacific. Melville was himself bound for adventures he could not have imagined. In the Marquesas he jumped ship and lived with cannibals as honored guest or as captive—he was not sure which—for a month. He escaped with his life, then worked his way to Tahiti and to Hawaii. He reached home, finally, a seaman aboard the U.S. frigate* United States, *sister ship of the* Constitution. *Ten years after his first taste of the sea he sat down to write the tale of a haunted whaling captain's search for a huge white whale.*

*In this excerpt from* Moby Dick, *Ahab's men lower the boats and pursue the first whale of the long voyage that ends in tragedy.*

It was a sight full of quick wonder and awe! The vast swells of the omnipotent sea; the surging, hollow roar they made, as they rolled along the eight gunwales, like gigantic bowls in a boundless bowling green; the brief suspended agony of the boat, as it would tip for an instant on the knifelike edge of the sharper waves, that almost seemed threatening to cut it in two; the sudden profound dip into the watery glens and hollows; the keen spurrings and goadings to gain the top of the opposite hill; the headlong, sledlike slide down its other side—all these, with the cries of the headsmen and harpooners, and the shuddering gasps of the oarsmen, with the wondrous sight of the ivory *Pequod* bearing down upon her boats with outstretched sails, like a wild hen after her screaming brood—all this was thrilling. Not the raw recruit, marching from the bosom of his wife into the fever heat of his first

*Anton Otto Fischer painted an American whaling ship "bearing down upon her boats with outstretched sails, like a wild hen after her screaming brood." Each boat carried harpooner, steersman, four men to row.*

battle; not the dead man's ghost encountering the first unknown phantom in the other world—neither of these can feel stranger and stronger emotions than that man does, who for the first time finds himself pulling into the charmed, churned circle of the hunted sperm whale.

The dancing white water made by the chase was now becoming more and more visible, owing to the increasing darkness of the dun cloud-shadows flung upon the sea. The jets of vapor no longer blended, but tilted everywhere to right and left; the whales seemed separating their wakes. The boats were pulled more apart; Starbuck giving chase to three whales running dead to leeward. Our sail was now set, and, with the still rising wind, we rushed along; the boat going with such madness through the water that the lee oars could scarcely be worked rapidly enough to escape being torn from the rowlocks.

Soon we were running through a suffusing wide veil of mist; neither ship nor boat to be seen.

"Give way, men," whispered Starbuck, drawing still further aft the sheet of his sail; "there is time to kill a fish yet before the squall comes. There's white water again!—close to! Spring!"

Soon after, two cries in quick succession on each side of us denoted that the other boats had got fast; but hardly were they overheard when with a lightninglike hurtling whisper Starbuck said: "Stand up!" and Queequeg, harpoon in hand, sprang to his feet.

Though not one of the oarsmen was then facing the life and death peril so close to them ahead, yet with their eyes on the intense countenance of the mate in the stern of the boat, they knew that the imminent instant had come; they heard, too, an enormous wallowing sound as of 50 elephants stirring in their litter. Meanwhile the boat was still booming through the mist, the waves curling and hissing around us like the erected crests of enraged serpents.

"That's his hump. *There, there*, give it to him!" whispered Starbuck.

A short rushing sound leaped out of the boat; it was the darted iron of Queequeg. Then all in one welded commotion came an invisible push from astern, while forward the boat seemed striking on a ledge; the sail collapsed and exploded; a gush of scalding vapor shot up nearby; something rolled and tumbled like an earthquake beneath us. The whole crew were half suffocated as they were tossed helter-skelter into the white curdling cream of the squall. Squall, whale, and harpoon had all blended together; and the whale, merely grazed by the iron, escaped.

Though completely swamped, the boat was nearly unharmed. Swimming round it we picked up the floating oars, and lashing them across the gunwale, tumbled back to our places. There we sat up to our knees in the sea, the water covering every rib and plank, so that to our downward gazing eyes the suspended craft seemed a coral boat grown up to us from the bottom of the ocean.

The wind increased to a howl; the waves dashed their bucklers together; the whole squall roared, forked, and crackled around us like a white fire upon the prairie, in which, unconsumed, we were burning; immortal in these jaws of death! In vain we hailed the other boats; as well roar to the live coals down the chimney of a flaming furnace as hail those boats in that storm. Meanwhile the driving scud, rack, and mist grew darker with the shadows of night; no sign of the ship could be seen. The rising sea forbade all attempts to bale out the boat. The oars were useless as propellers, performing now the office of life preservers. So, cutting the lashing of the waterproof match keg, after many failures Starbuck contrived to ignite the lamp in the lantern; then stretching it on a waif pole, handed it to Queequeg as the standard-bearer of this forlorn hope. There, then, he sat, holding up that imbecile candle in the heart of that almighty forlornness. There, then, he sat, the sign and symbol of a man without faith, hopelessly holding up hope in the midst of despair.

Wet, drenched through, and shivering cold, despairing of ship or boat, we lifted up our eyes as the dawn came on. The mist still spread over the sea, the empty lantern lay crushed in the bottom of the boat. Suddenly Queequeg started to his feet, hollowing his hand to his ear. We all heard a faint creaking, as of ropes and yards hitherto muffled by the storm. The sound came nearer and nearer; the thick mists were dimly parted by a huge, vague form. Affrighted, we all sprang into the sea as the ship at last loomed into view, bearing right down upon us within a distance of not much more than its length.

Floating on the waves we saw the abandoned boat, as for one instant it tossed and gaped beneath the ship's bows like a chip at the base of a cataract; and then the vast hull rolled over it, and it was seen no more till it came up weltering astern. Again we swam for it, were dashed against it by the seas, and were at last taken up and safely landed on board. Ere the squall came close to, the other boats had cut loose from their fish and returned to the ship in good time. The ship had given us up, but was still cruising, if haply it might light upon some token of our perishing—an oar or a lance pole.

*Norman Rockwell painted a wild-eyed harpooner not unlike Queequeg to illustrate a 1940 story for the* Post.

*Castaways! Shipwrecked sailors make for port in an open boat, in an illustration by A. O. Fischer.*

# The Face of the East

## BY JOSEPH CONRAD

*Conrad served 20 years in the merchant marine before retiring in 1894 to devote full time to writing. By that time he had anglicized his Russian-Polish name—he was born Józef Teodor Konrad Nalecz Korzeniowski—and acquired a command of the English language. He had also acquired a master's certificate and an encyclopedic knowledge of ships and the sea. The following*

*excerpt is from a 1902 story, "Youth." The men in the small boats are officers and crew of a merchant ship that has burned at sea. The narrator is the very young second mate who is placed in charge of one boat and told to steer for Bangkok.*

I need not tell you what it is to be knocking about in an open boat. I remember nights and days of calm, when we pulled, we pulled, and the boat seemed to stand still, as if bewitched within the circle of the sea horizon. I remember the heat, the deluge of rainsqualls that kept us baling for dear life (but filled our water cask), and I remember 16 hours on end with a

*East is East and West is West—but they do meet in the harbors of the world where ships of different registry dock side by side.*

mouth dry as a cinder and a steering oar over the stern to keep my first command head on to a breaking sea. I did not know how good a man I was till then. I remember the drawn faces, the dejected figures of my two men, and I remember my youth and the feeling that will never come back any more—the feeling that I could last for ever, outlast the sea, the earth, and all men; the deceitful feeling that lures us on to joys, to perils, to love, to vain effort—to death; the triumphant conviction of strength, the heat of life in the handful of dust, the glow in the heart that with every year grows dim, grows cold, grows small, and expires—and expires, too soon, too soon—before life itself.

"And this is how I see the East. I have seen its secret places and have looked into its very soul; but now I see it always from a small boat, a high outline of mountains, blue and afar in the morning; like faint mist at noon; a jagged wall of purple at sunset. I have the feel of the oar in my hand, the vision of a scorching blue sea in my eyes. And I see a bay, a wide bay, smooth as glass and polished like ice, shimmering in the dark. A red light burns far off upon the gloom of the land, and the night is soft and warm. We drag at the oars with aching arms, and suddenly a puff of wind, a puff faint and tepid and laden with strange odors of blossoms, of

aromatic wood, comes out of the still night—the first sigh of the East on my face. That I can never forget. It was impalpable and enslaving, like a charm, like a whispered promise of mysterious delight.

"We had been pulling this finishing spell for eleven hours. Two pulled, and he whose turn it was to rest sat at the tiller. We had made out the red light in that bay and steered for it, guessing it must mark some small coasting port. We passed two vessels, outlandish and high-sterned, sleeping at anchor, and, approaching the light now very dim, ran the boat's nose against the end of a jutting wharf. We were blind with fatigue. My men dropped the oars and fell off the thwarts as if dead. I made fast to a pile. A current rippled softly. The scented obscurity of the shore was grouped into vast masses, a density of colossal clumps of vegetation, probably—mute and fantastic shapes. And at their foot the semicircle of a beach gleamed faintly, like an illusion. There was not a light, not a stir, not a sound. The mysterious East faced me, perfumed like a flower, silent like death, dark like a grave.

"And I sat weary beyond expression, exulting like a conqueror, sleepless and entranced as if before a profound, a fateful enigma.

"A splashing of oars, a measured dip reverberating on the level of water, intensified by the silence of the shore into loud claps, made me jump up. A boat, a European boat, was coming in. I invoked the name of the dead; I hailed: *Judea* ahoy! A thin shout answered.

"It was the captain. I had beaten the flagship by three hours, and I was glad to hear the old man's voice again, tremulous and tired. 'Is it you, Marlow?' 'Mind the end of that jetty, sir,' I cried.

"He approached cautiously, and brought up with the deep-sea lead line which we had saved—for the underwriters. I eased my painter and fell alongside. He sat, a broken figure at the stern, wet with dew, his hands clasped in his lap. His men were asleep already. 'I had a terrible time of it,' he murmured. 'Mahon is behind—

not very far.' We conversed in whispers, in low whispers, as if afraid to wake up the land. Guns, thunder, earthquakes would not have awakened the men just then.

"Looking round as we talked, I saw away at sea a bright light traveling in the night. 'There's a steamer passing the bay,' I said. She was not passing, she was entering, and she even came close and anchored. 'I wish,' said the old man, 'you would find out whether she is English. Perhaps they could give us a passage somewhere.' He seemed nervously anxious. So by dint of punching and kicking I started one of my men into a state of somnambulism, and giving him an oar, took

" 'Castaway crew of an English barque burnt at sea. We came here tonight. I am the second mate. The captain is in the longboat, and wishes to know if you would give us a passage somewhere.'

" 'Oh, my goodness! I say. . . .This is the *Celestial* from Singapore on her return trip. I'll arrange with your captain in the morning, . . .and, . . . I say, . . . did you hear me just now?'

" 'I should think the whole bay heard you.'

" 'I thought you were a shore boat. Now, look here—this infernal lazy scoundrel of a caretaker has gone to sleep again—curse him. The light is out, and I nearly ran foul of the end of this damned jetty. This is

*Joseph Conrad wrote of poverty and hard physical labor as well as heroic adventure on land and at sea.*

another and pulled toward the lights of the steamer.

"There was a murmur of voices in her, metallic hollow clangs of the engine room, footsteps on the deck. Her ports shone, round like dilated eyes. Shapes moved about, and there was a shadowy man high up on the bridge. He heard my oars.

"And then, before I could open my lips, the East spoke to me, but it was in a Western voice. A torrent of words was poured into the enigmatical, the fateful silence; outlandish, angry words, mixed with words and even whole sentences of good English, less strange but even more surprising. The voice swore and cursed violently; it riddled the solemn peace of the bay by a volley of abuse. It began by calling me Pig, and from that went crescendo into unmentionable adjectives—in English. The man up there raged aloud in two languages, and with a sincerity in his fury that almost convinced me I had, in some way, sinned against the harmony of the universe. I could hardly see him, but began to think he would work himself into a fit.

"Suddenly he ceased, and I could hear him snorting and blowing like a porpoise. I said—

" 'What steamer is this, pray?'

" 'Eh? What's this? And who are you?'

the third time he plays me this trick. Now, I ask you, can anybody stand this kind of thing? It's enough to drive a man out of his mind. I'll report him. . . .I'll get the Assistant Resident to give him the sack, by . . . ! See—there's no light. It's out, isn't it? I take you to witness the light's out. There should be a light, you know. A red light on the——'

" 'There was a light,' I said, mildly.

" 'But it's out, man! What's the use of talking like this? You can see for yourself it's out—don't you? If you had to take a valuable steamer along this godforsaken coast you would want a light, too. I'll kick him from end to end of this miserable wharf. You'll see if I don't. I will——'

" 'May I tell my captain you'll take us?' I broke in.

" 'Yes, I'll take you. Good night,' he said, brusquely.

"I pulled back, made fast again to the jetty, and then went to sleep at last. I had faced the silence of the East. I had heard some of its language. But when I opened my eyes again the silence was as complete as though it had never been broken. I was lying in a flood of light, and the sky had never looked so far, so high, before. I opened my eyes and lay without moving.

"And then I saw the men of the East—they were

*Anton Otto Fischer painted rusty freighters that plowed through the sea, as well as graceful clippers that skimmed over it.*

*Seamen glimpsed a strange and colorful world when their ships docked at Asian ports.*

looking at me. The whole length of the jetty was full of people. I saw brown, bronze, yellow faces, the black eyes, the glitter, the color of an Eastern crowd. And all these beings stared without a murmur, without a sigh, without a movement. They stared down at the boats, at the sleeping men who at night had come to them from the sea. Nothing moved. The fronds of palms stood still against the sky. Not a branch stirred along the shore, and the brown roofs of hidden houses peeped through the green foliage, through the big leaves that hung shining and still like leaves forged of heavy metal. This was the East of the ancient navigators, so old, so mysterious, resplendent and somber, living and unchanged, full of danger and promise. And these were the men. I sat up suddenly. A wave of movement passed through the crowd from end to end, passed along the heads, swayed the bodies, ran along the jetty like a ripple on the water, like a breath of wind on a field—and all was still again. I see it now—the wide sweep of the bay, the glittering sands, the wealth of green infinite and varied, the sea blue like the sea of a dream, the crowd of attentive faces, the blaze of vivid color—the water reflecting it all, the curve of the shore, the jetty, the high-sterned outlandish craft floating still, and the three boats with the tired men from the West sleeping, unconscious of the land and the people and of the violence of sunshine. They slept thrown across the thwarts, curled on bottom boards, in the careless attitudes of death. The head of the old skipper, leaning back in the stern of the longboat, had fallen on his breast, and he looked as though he would never wake. Farther out old Mahon's face was upturned to the sky, with the long white beard spread out on his breast, as though he had been shot where he sat at the tiller; and a man, all in a heap in the bows of the boat, slept with both arms embracing the stemhead and with his cheek laid on the gunwale. The East looked at them without a sound.

"I have known its fascination since; I have seen the mysterious shores, the still water, the lands of brown nations, where a stealthy Nemesis lies in wait, pursues, overtakes so many of the conquering race, who are proud of their wisdom, of their knowledge, of their strength. But for me all the East is contained in that vision of my youth. It is all in that moment when I opened my young eyes on it. I came upon it from a tussle with the sea—and I was young—and I saw it looking at me. And this is all that is left of it! Only a moment; a moment of strength, of romance, of glamour—of youth! . . . A flick of sunshine upon a strange shore, the time to remember, the time for a sigh, and—good-bye!—Night—Good-bye . . . !"

He drank.

"Ah! The good old time—the good old time. Youth and the sea. Glamour and the sea! The good, strong sea, the salt, bitter sea, that could whisper to you and roar at you and knock your breath out of you."

He drank again.

"By all that's wonderful it is the sea, I believe, the sea itself—or is it youth alone? Who can tell? But you here—you all had something out of life: money, love—whatever one gets on shore—and, tell me, wasn't that the best time, that time when we were young at sea; young and had nothing, on the sea that gives nothing, except hard knocks—and sometimes a chance to feel your strength—that only—what you all regret?"

And we all nodded at him: the man of finance, the man of accounts, the man of law; we all nodded at him over the polished table that like a still sheet of brown water reflected our faces, lined, wrinkled; our faces marked by toil, by deceptions, by success, by love; our weary eyes looking always, looking anxiously for something out of life, that while it is expected is already gone—has passed unseen, in a sigh, in a flash—together with the youth, with the strength, with the romance of illusions.

*Death in the sea supports life in, on the sea. William Goadby Lawrence painted a voracious blue marlin for the* Post *in 1942.*

# Old Man, Big Fish

## BY ERNEST HEMINGWAY

*A passion for sport fishing led Hemingway into a deep and abiding love of the sea and a profound respect for men who earn a living on her. Hemingway was in his thirties, already famous as the author of several widely read books, when he moved to Key West, Florida. There, and later in Cuba, his best friends were fishermen and his happiest days were spent aboard his boat, the* Pilar, *pursuing giant marlin in the warm Gulf Stream. The Old Man and the Sea, published in 1952, owes its very special quality to Hemingway's masterful descriptions of sea and sky, and to his understanding of the ways of fish and fishermen.*

He looked across the sea and knew how alone he was now. But he could see the prisms in the deep dark water and the line stretching ahead and the strange undulation of the calm. The clouds were building up now for the trade wind and he looked ahead and saw a flight of wild ducks etching themselves against the sky over the water, then blurring, then etching again, and he knew no man was ever alone on the sea.

He thought of how some men feared being out of sight of land in a small boat and knew they were right in the months of sudden bad weather. But now they were in hurricane months and, when there are no hurricanes, the weather of hurricane months is the best of all the year.

If there is a hurricane you always see the signs of it in the sky for days ahead, if you are at sea. They do not see it ashore because they do not know what to look for, he thought. The land must make a difference too,

*Whether he makes use of net or baited line, the small-boat fisherman finds his work hard, cold, and lonely. The hours are long, the rewards uncertain.*

in the shape of the clouds. But we have no hurricane coming now.

He looked at the sky and saw the white cumulus built like friendly piles of ice cream and high above were the thin feathers of the cirrus against the high September sky.

"Light *brisa*," he said. "Better weather for me than for you, fish."

His left hand was still cramped, but he was unknotting it slowly.

I hate a cramp, he thought. It is a treachery of one's own body. It is humiliating before others to have a diarrhea from ptomaine poisoning or to vomit from it. But a cramp, he thought of it as a *calambre*, humiliates oneself especially when one is alone.

If the boy were here he could rub it for me and loosen it down from the forearm, he thought. But it will loosen up.

Then, with his right hand he felt the difference in the pull of the line before he saw the slant change in the water. Then, as he leaned against the line and slapped his left hand hard and fast against his thigh he saw the line slanting slowly upward.

"He's coming up," he said. "Come on hand. Please come on."

The line rose slowly and steadily and then the surface of the ocean bulged ahead of the boat and the fish came out. He came out unendingly and water poured from his sides. He was bright in the sun and his head and back were dark purple and in the sun the stripes on his sides showed wide and a light lavender. His sword was as long as a baseball bat and tapered like a rapier and he rose his full length from the water and then re-entered

it, smoothly, like a diver and the old man saw the great scythe-blade of his tail go under and the line commenced to race out.

"He is two feet longer than the skiff," the old man said. The line was going out fast but steadily and the fish was not panicked. The old man was trying with both hands to keep the line just inside of breaking strength. He knew that if he could not slow the fish with a steady pressure the fish could take out all the line and break it.

He is a great fish and I must convince him, he thought. I must never let him learn his strength nor what he could do if he made his run. If I were him I would put in everything now and go until something broke. But, thank God, they are not as intelligent as we who kill them; although they are more noble and more able.

The man had seen many great fish. He had seen many that weighed more than a thousand pounds and he had caught two of that size in his life, but never alone. Now alone, and out of sight of land, he was fast to the biggest fish that he had ever seen and bigger than he had ever heard of, and his left hand was still as tight as the gripped claws of an eagle.

It will uncramp though, he thought. Surely it will uncramp to help my right hand. There are three things that are brothers: the fish and my two hands. It must uncramp. It is unworthy of it to be cramped. The fish had slowed again and was going at his usual pace.

I wonder why he jumped, the old man thought. He jumped almost as though to show me how big he was. I know now, anyway, he thought. I wish I could show him what sort of man I am. But then he would see the cramped hand. Let him think I am more man than I am and I will be so. I wish I was the fish, he thought, with everything he has against only my will and my intelligence.

He settled comfortably against the wood and took his suffering as it came and the fish swam steadily and the boat moved slowly through the dark water. There was a small sea rising with the wind coming up from the east and at noon the old man's left hand was uncramped.

"Bad news for you, fish," he said and shifted the line over the sacks that covered his shoulders.

He was comfortable but suffering, although he did not admit the suffering at all.

"I am not religious," he said. "But I will say ten Our Fathers and ten Hail Marys that I should catch this fish, and I promise to make a pilgrimage to the Virgin of Cobre if I catch him. That is a promise."

*The simple realities of the fisherman's life appeal to artists as well as writers. Mead Schaeffer painted this 1949* Post *cover.*

He commenced to say his prayers mechanically. Sometimes he would be so tired that he could not remember the prayer and then he would say them fast so that they would come automatically. Hail Marys are easier to say than Our Fathers, he thought.

"Hail Mary full of Grace the Lord is with thee. Blessed art thou among women and blessed is the fruit of thy womb, Jesus. Holy Mary, Mother of God, pray for us sinners now and at the hour of our death. Amen."

Then he added, "Blessed Virgin, pray for the death of this fish. Wonderful though he is."

# About the Illustrations

This book is a tribute to many talented artists who helped make *The Saturday Evening Post* America's favorite magazine. In particular it honors Anton Otto Fischer whose marine paintings appeared in the magazine between 1912 and 1952.

Born in Germany in 1882 and orphaned at an early age, Fischer ran away to sea and served eight years aboard sailing ships. Later, in the U.S., he taught seamanship and worked aboard racing yachts while saving money to study art, first in Paris and then with American illustrator Howard Pyle. Fischer's paintings of sailing ships are beautiful and they are also totally authentic; he knew the feel and weight and purpose of each rope and bit of canvas he depicted. Fischer knew steel and steam and diesel also; he went back to sea in 1942 as official artist for the U.S. Coast Guard and served aboard a cutter that successfully attacked an enemy U-boat in the North Atlantic.

Illustrator McClelland Barclay, born in St. Louis in 1891, also went to sea as an official artist in World War II. He served with the Navy in the Pacific and died aboard an LST that was torpedoed.

Painter Gordon Grant was born in San Francisco in 1875. He fell in love with ships and the sea as a youngster, when his father sent him to school in Scotland by way of a 4½-month voyage around Cape Horn under sail. Grant began his career as a war correspondent and newspaper artist, but as a mature painter he specialized in marine subjects. His pictures of sailing ships appeared in the *Post* between 1933 and 1937.

Included in this book are examples of the work of other *Post* illustrators and cover artists who were not primarily marine painters but who sometimes used the sea as background or subject: Karl Anderson, E. L. Bloomster, Charles Livingston Bull, John Cecil Clay, John Clymer, Ritchie Cooper, Anthony Cucchi, Harvey T. Dunn, Walter H. Everett, Harrison Fisher, Peter Fountain, George Gibbs, J. J. Gould, F. R. Gruger, George Hughes, E. M. (Elbert McGran) Jackson, Harry B. Lachman, John LaGatta, William Goadby Lawrence, Frank X. Leyendecker, J. C. (Joseph Christian) Leyendecker, Emlen McConnell, Clyde E. MacLellan, Guernsey Moore, Dale Nichols, Edward Penfield, Coles Phillips, James Preston, Ellen Pyle, Joseph J. Ray, Ken Riley, Norman Rockwell, F. Rogers, Dick Sargent, Mead Schaeffer, John E. Sheridan, Henry J. Soulen, Ben Stahl, Frank Street, H. W. Tilson, Lawrence Toney, Clarence Underwood, Sarah S. Stilwell Weber, James Williamson, Mrs. K. R. Wireman. In a few cases there is no record of an artist's name or the signature is illegible, and in a few cases the illustration was originally part of an advertisement.

With the exception of the Howard Pyle painting on page 105, all illustrations in this book are from the pages of *The Saturday Evening Post*. The pictures reproduced in two colors—often red and black—were magazine covers prior to 1926 when new presses made full-color covers possible. The pictures in full color are post-1926 magazine covers, illustrations, or advertisements. The small black and white pieces are page decorations that appeared at the beginnings or ends of articles between 1898 and 1910.

# Acknowledgments

"Hornblower and the Penalty of Failure" by C. S. Forester is reprinted with permission of Harold Matson Company, Inc. Copyright © 1948 by Curtis Publishing Company; copyright © 1950 by C. S. Forester; copyright renewed © 1978 by Dorothy Forester.

"All about Sailing" is "The Story of Sailing" by James Thurber. Copyright © 1942 by James Thurber. Copyright © 1970 by Helen W. Thurber and Rosemary Thurber. From *My World—And Welcome to It* published by Harcourt Brace Jovanovich. Originally published in *The Bermudian.*

"The Perilous Voyage of the Mayflower" is condensed from *One Small Candle* by Thomas J. Fleming. Copyright © 1963 by Thomas J. Fleming. Condensation reprinted from the December 1963 *Readers Digest* by permission of Paul R. Reynolds, Inc., 12 East 41st Street, New York 10017.

"Men Against the Sea" is an excerpt from the book *Men Against the Sea* by Charles Nordhoff and James Norman Hall. Copyright © 1933, 1934 by Charles Nordhoff and James Norman Hall. Copyright renewed © 1961, 1962. Reprinted with permission of Little, Brown and Company.

"Try Building a Chinese Junk" is an excerpt from *The Famous Adventures of Richard Halliburton.* Copyright © 1940 by Bobbs-Merrill Company; copyright renewed © 1968. Reprinted with permission of Bobbs-Merrill Company.

"The Rough Crossing" is reprinted with permission of Charles Scribner's Sons from *The Stories of F. Scott Fitzgerald.* Copyright © 1929 by Curtis Publishing Company.

"They Are All Gone" is an excerpt from Walter Lord's foreword to *The Only Way to Cross* by John Maxtone-Graham. Copyright © 1972 by John Maxtone-Graham. Reprinted with permission of MacMillan Publishing Co., Inc.

"Old Man, Big Fish" is an excerpt from *The Old Man and the Sea* by Ernest Hemingway. Copyright © 1952 by Ernest Hemingway. Reprinted with permission of Charles Scribner's Sons.

Along with copyrighted stories and articles from *The Saturday Evening Post*, this book contains some original material and some selections that are in the public domain. We are grateful to the authors and their heirs or representatives who have granted permission for material to appear again.

"The Flying Dutchman" by Howard Pyle first appeared in *Collier's*; it is reproduced here through the courtesy of the Delaware Art Museum, Wilmington, Delaware. Except for this painting and the photographs of restored sailing ships, all illustrations are from *The Saturday Evening Post* and are the copyrighted property of The Curtis Publishing Company or The Saturday Evening Post Company.